Love is a Journey:
Couples Facing Cancer

By Jan Latona, Ph.D. & Gary J. Stricklin, Ph.D.

Greyrock Publishing
Fort Collins, Colorado

Love is a Journey: Couples Facing Cancer

Published by Greyrock Publishing
PO Box 272964
Fort Collins, Colorado 80527-2964

Web site: http://www.couplesfacingcancer.com

Printed in the United States of America

Library of Congress Cataloging-in-Publication Data

Latona, Jan
  Love is a Journey: Couples Facing Cancer

  1. Cancer — Popular Works. 2. Cancer — Psychological Aspects.
  I. Stricklin, Gary J.
ISBN 0-9673715-0-3 (pbk.)

616.994   99-66209

"Cancer may kill me, but I'm not going to let it ruin my life."

Peter Quirk (1996)

Born: October 1948
Died: October 1997 of cancer

Acknowledgments

The authors of this book are deeply grateful to the many people who have supported the development of this book.

Our gratitude goes to the couples who participated in the original Couples Facing Cancer™ groups: Gail and Pete (deceased), Barb and Lanny, Janet and Brian (deceased), Kemper and Cathy, Carl and Jody, Wayne and Jill, Cheryle and Mike, Jane and Brian, Karen and Jonathan. Thank you for your courage, your laughter, and all you taught us. We love you.

Thank you to our parents, children, multiple extended families, friends, and helpers who supported, loved, and encouraged us through 1997 when Gary was in intensive cancer treatment — and then told us to go for it and write a book!

We appreciate our employer, Employee Assistance Programs International, for providing facilities in which the CFC groups could meet and for encouraging us to follow our dream. Our EAPI colleagues and friends have been invaluable for their advice, consultation, and loving support.

We have learned much from the writings and teachings of the Commonweal Cancer Support Center Tradecraft Program; Rachel Naomi Remen, M.D. was instrumental in teaching us how to support people dealing with cancer and has provided a role model through her work, which is focused on changing how the world confronts illness and life. The teachings of Bernie Siegel, M.D., were helpful in providing grounding with the overwhelming load of the cancer experience. David Whyte's writings on living with heart and courage were most influential.

Val McCullough, Ed.D.; Barry Berns, M.D.; Marc Salkin, Ph.D.; George Hunter, L.P.C.; Robert Marschke, M.D.; Maria Cox, M.A.; Lisa Temple, O.M.D.; and Gregory Long, D.E. (Drummer Extraordinaire) contributed their healing wisdom and skills in our journeys with cancer and with this book.

Thank you also to Colorado Independent Publishers Association, Robert Howard for cover design, Steve Thompson Photography for the authors' photo, and Ink & Scribe for editing and book design.

Introduction

The journey that cancer presents a couple is difficult at best. The experience of cancer and treatment is challenging to the individuals and the relationship. Each of these entities (the patient, the spouse, and the relationship) will feel battered by the stresses and strains of this journey. Expect that there will be many tears, long nights, and angry exchanges, along with intense love, determination, laughter, commitment, and joy.

In this book, we have provided a travelogue of points along the journey. As with any travel brochure, it tells you what to expect; but as with any journey, the actual experience is comprised of events unique to that particular trip and the individuals involved. The couple may find that they revisit some stages and skip others. Some couples may travel this journey several times and visit the points along the journey over and over, depending on the course that the cancer takes. A couple may travel this journey once in a lifetime, several times in quick succession, or repeated times with many years in between.

Each couple must complete the journey described in this book in their own way. There is no magic formula. It is tempting to say, just follow these ten steps or those four principles, and you will be guaranteed a successful and happy journey. Would that it could be so easy.

The authors of this book have traveled the journey several times. Both have traveled the journey in relationship with other partners and, as of this writing, one time as a couple together. Jan traveled this journey with her husband, Alan, on a path that moved quickly from diagnosis to Alan's death. Gary traveled the journey briefly from diagnosis to remission in his first marriage. Jan and Gary traveled this journey together from Gary's second diagnosis to remission once again.

The concept of the journey has been garnered from the authors' own experiences and the experiences of the many couples they have worked with and learned from as therapists, speakers, and group leaders. The result is a body of knowledge about this process learned from those living the experience.

The wish of the authors is that you, the readers, will use this information to guide your own journeys. Use this resource, and the many others available to you, to travel your journey bolstered by love, joy, and courage. Reach out and use resources in ways that work best for you as individuals and as a couple. You will find resources in the form of books, pamphlets, spoken words, groups, hugs, the Internet, professionals, friends, family, strangers, alternative healers, poems, spiritual guides, other couples, and survivors. Experience has shown us that using supportive resources does make a difference. This is not a journey to be traveled alone. There is much love and compassion available to you that will not only ease the burden of the journey, but will also enhance your living and loving when the journey is completed.

Preface

When a person is in a committed relationship and he or she receives the diagnosis of cancer, three human entities are affected.

One is the person with the cancer diagnosis, whom we shall call the patient.

Another is the partner in the relationship, whom we will refer to as the spouse.

The third entity is that magical chemistry between two people, which we will call the relationship.

Each of these entities has a certain level of emotional health and resilience at the point in time when the diagnosis is given. All of these entities will now be faced with challenges and opportunities that will change them forever.

In this book, we share with you the stories of couples faced with cancer, the dynamics of their lives, and the paths they have followed. Cancer does not respect age, gender, race, professional accomplishments, or family responsibilities. It lands on the life of a couple unbidden and unwelcome.

Paul and Geri learned of Paul's cancer just a year before he died, when his cancer had already metastasized beyond what treatment could overpower. Their three children were teenagers, and Geri had spent the twenty-five years of her married life raising them, taking care of household and family needs, and volunteering much of her time to several community services she supported. Paul was in the computer and engineering field and also led a very active life, volunteering for community activities, hunting, and hiking in the Colorado mountains. Paul and Geri felt strongly about many things, lived fully, and were totally committed to their family and the raising of their children.

Larry and Beth married several years ago, the second marriage for each, and between them they had five adult sons and daughters. Larry's cancer diagnosis had occurred prior to meeting Beth, so their relationship began with cancer as a part of it. His treatment extended over a period of ten years, with minimal cancer activity for some of the time periods within those years and intense treatment at other times. Larry and Beth have been very active in their lives together, and their hearts have been passionate about work and family. They have risked major career changes, confronted cancer and treatment issues head-on, and faced off with medical providers whenever a provider didn't "get it." Larry's cancer has now begun to gain ground and may be beyond treatments that are known today, so, as you can imagine, Larry and Beth are at a new point in their journey with cancer, with each other, and with life itself.

Walter and Jane are in their late twenties; they married each other four years ago and have children who are three and one and one-half years old. Walter and Jane are busy with careers, family, extended family, and recreational activities. Three months ago, Walter had two malignant moles surgically removed that revealed melanoma. He started an eighteen-month regimen of three self-injections per week of an immuno-chemotherapy medication. Walter and Jane are fiercely committed to their family and are still reeling from the shock of his news and the terror that has invaded their young family.

Tom and Judy, in their late 40s, married about six years ago. Both are actively involved in their respective careers and with family, friends, and community and church activities. These activities remain their passion even though Judy's cancer diagnosis has intruded into the midst of them. Judy was diagnosed with colon cancer about four months ago, at which time a very optimistic prognosis was given. It was anticipated that treatment would be minimal and should provide no major life disruption. After living with this alarming but hopeful prediction, she was recently told the cancer was not responding the way it needed to and that her treatment options needed to be far more invasive. Tom and Judy are living not only with the fear of cancer but with the adjustment to what a colonectomy surgery will mean to their lives and their relationship.

These four stories set the stage for how cancer can enter the life of a couple. Cancer happens to real people with real lives. The rest of this book will give you an intimate view of how many different couples have faced the challenge. You will share in their successes and failures. You will be given tools and guidelines to assist you in nourishing your love relationship in the midst of the challenge.

Disclaimer

This book is designed to provide information in regard to the subject matter covered. It is sold with the understanding that the publisher and authors are not rendering legal or professional psychological services. If other expert assistance is required, the services of a competent professional should be sought.

It is not the purpose of this book to provide all that is needed to support a couple facing cancer. There are many and varied sources of information and assistance. Readers are encouraged to use the Resources and Recommended Reading sections of this book as tools for locating helpers. What is right for one individual or couple may not be right for another. The ideas in this book can serve as a starting place; use those that work for you, and discard those that are not a good fit. Be sure to seek expert and competent medical and psychological assistance and care.

This text should be used only as a general guide for self-help. Licensed professionals are available in your community to assist with concerns that are specific to your particular circumstance. The authors and Greyrock Publishing shall have neither liability nor responsibility to any person or entity with respect to loss or damage caused, or alleged to be caused, directly or indirectly by the information contained in this book.

If you do not wish to be bound by the above, you may return this book to the publisher for a full refund.

Contents

CHAPTER 1

THE MAP OF THE JOURNEY

The travels of a couple facing cancer will lead them down many roads. Some are long; some are short. They can be treacherous or gently rolling. The scenery contains fear, determination, anger, love, frustration, togetherness, loneliness, joy, misunderstanding, intensity, and distancing. It helps to have a map.

In this chapter we provide you with a map (see page 6). Knowing where you are helps to understand where you have been, where you are going, and what the challenges are to you, as a couple, at your current point in the journey. The locations on the Experiential Map are: The News, Team Rally, Marathon and Sledgehammers, and Life Threat, followed by Destination: Death or Destination: Life, Cure, Remission.

NEWS

The journey always starts from the point of NEWS. The news may come from a medical report, a doctor's statement, or self-discovery. When the news is received, the human response for both the patient and the spouse is numbness and shock. This response is followed, sometimes very quickly, by feelings such as fear, anger, sadness, and panic.

TEAM RALLY

When the individuals learn more about the situation, including the type of cancer, the level of development of the disease, and the treatment recommendations, the couple often moves into TEAM RALLY. This is a time of pulling together, facing the situation, and feeling strength and determination. There is often a sense of "we can beat this thing; just tell us what to do and we will do it. We will support each other."

When a couple has been in conflict previous to receiving the NEWS, they may pull together to confront this external foe. However, if the couple does not feel a sense of being a team, each of the members is likely to feel a longing for that team relationship and may resent its absence.

MARATHON AND SLEDGEHAMMERS

The word MARATHON represents the journey of day-to-day life over time. It includes the normal life events that continue happening in the midst of the unexpected illness and the treatments. During the MARATHON, it takes stamina to meet the demands of weariness, chores, multiple losses, and fear. The couple must find ways to adapt to these demands.

The shock and numbness of the earlier stages wears off, and couples find they are not able to maintain the pace needed with extra effort and adrenaline alone. Changes need to be made in lifestyle if an active phase of the disease or treatment continues for a long time. Life continues; shopping needs to be done, the grass grows and needs to be cut, the kids' activities continue, job demands are present, the house gets dirty, and laundry piles up. Accommodations are necessary to integrate cancer and treatment into the daily life patterns of the household.

The MARATHON phase of the journey may be short-term or may extend over many years, depending on the course of the cancer. During this time, SLEDGEHAMMERS are the unexpected news, events, or changes in course. While we humans like to think we will get directions and a course that we can gear up to and count on, cancer treatment often does not have a rhythm or predictability. SLEDGEHAMMERS come from unexpected developments of the disease, changes in treatment strategies, unpredicted impacts of the disease or the treatment, financial burdens, activity changes, and the behaviors of our families, friends and co-workers.

LIFE THREAT

LIFE THREAT is the phase of the journey when the patient's life is in jeopardy. Many couples never face this situation if the cancer is caught early or if the treatment is successful early. Others will experience this, however. It is a time when the patient's body is threatened. The threat may come from the cancer itself or from the impact of necessary but dangerous treatment.

The couple is once again called to rally, to make difficult

decisions, to revive courage and determination. This may be the first time that the possibility of death becomes a reality.

DESTINATION: DEATH
DESTINATION: LIFE, CURE, REMISSION

There are two possible final destinations for this journey. Both allow the opportunity to find peace and joy as individuals and as a couple.

Paying attention throughout the journey to the resources and activities that promote physical, spiritual, emotional, and relationship health will lead to arrival at the place of peace and joy for both partners. This is not to say that DESTINATION: DEATH is not full of sadness, loss, and all that accompanies losing one's chosen life partner. But it is possible to hold that and experience it within the cradle of going there together in love.

Hopefully, those couples so blessed as to return to health will take with them the lessons that a journey with cancer can teach, ways to hold each other and their life experiences in joy and in awe.

SUMMARY

The couple that is aware of the journey stages can develop activities and processes to deal with the challenges and use them as opportunities (yes, opportunities!) to build a better relationship, deepen spiritual beliefs, and open themselves to living in love.

HOW TO USE THIS BOOK

In each chapter you will find short stories about real couples who have been challenged with cancer. As you read about the intimate details of their lives, consider your own relationship and life experiences. Notice how you are the same or different. Be open to what you can learn from what worked for them and what didn't.

Guidance about what works and what does not work is provided in each and every chapter. The information and suggestions have been gleaned from the experiences of real people facing the real challenges of the journey with cancer.

Finally, every chapter contains activities to keep your love relationship alive and growing. There is space provided so you can jot down your thoughts and ideas. Write them down while they are fresh. They can then serve as the springboard for discussions, actions, or more in-depth thinking and writing.

The Map of the Journey: Couples Facing Cancer™

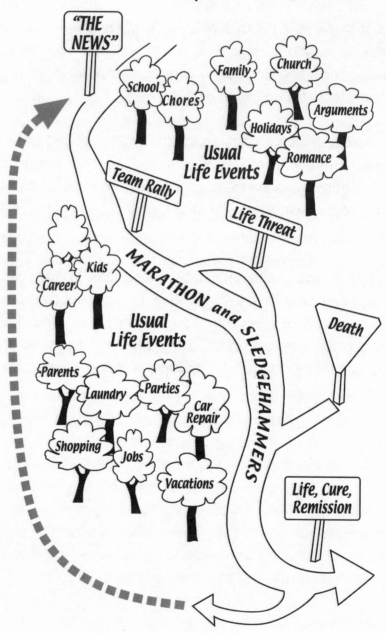

CHAPTER 2

TOOLS FOR THE JOURNEY

There are tools available for you to use on this emotional, as well as physical, journey. The tools described in this chapter are to be used throughout the journey with cancer, rather than saved for a specific time or situation.

If you were taking a journey on foot, you would be advised to wear good shoes, drink water regularly, and take appropriate rests throughout the hike. By doing these things you are increasing the probability that you will feel better throughout the hike, maintain the stamina to complete the journey, and reduce the likelihood for injuries. The same applies to the journey with cancer. By using the tools described, you will gain the same advantages, as individuals and as a couple, to meet the challenges of this journey. As with any journey, these tools are not magic; the road is still long and the hills very steep and tiring. There is no easy ride, no shortcut when facing cancer, and each couple must find the best way for them to travel as individuals and as a team. The tools described in this chapter are basic and available to all. Take the time to use them; practice. Check the list periodically to see what you've overlooked lately, and get assistance from friends or counselors for the tools that are new, awkward, or uncomfortable for you.

Use these tools to keep yourselves and your relationship

physically and emotionally as healthy as possible. Doing so will help you meet the many challenges, cope with difficulties that may feel overwhelming at times, and be able to be open to love and joy during this journey.

Sometimes it is tempting to decide to just tough it out and think that the good times will come later when this is over. This is a bad idea. Your time with cancer may be lengthy or short term, but whichever it is — it will change your life forever. You now know that it can really happen, that you and your spouse are vulnerable to a life-threatening illness. The denial with which most of us live has been shattered. By using these tools you will be strengthening, building, and broadening the way the two of you face death and live life.

TOOL ONE: ACCEPTANCE

It is natural to have very intense emotions when facing a life-threatening illness such as cancer. It may even seem that your feelings, actions, reactions, and interactions are so strong as to be irrational.

Carol cried deep, racking sobs for what seemed like days during times of distressing news and change.

Judy, Larry, and Bruce went through periods of being hyper-conscious of every body twitch and change, fearing it might be cancer.

Larry traveled a lot and attempted to see everyone and engage in all his favorite activities.

Jane started snapping at co-workers.

Carol couldn't concentrate well.

Many, many examples could be given, none of which are signs of mental illness or not coping. These behaviors are normal ways of coping with an abnormal situation. The goal is not to stop them as soon as possible in order to get back to your old self, or to start acting more like the rest of the world. The goal is to trust yourself and your body. Be patient with yourself and observe how this attitude might be helpful over time.

It is very painful for spouses to experience their partners living out such extreme distress. It's tempting to try to fix things to make them feel better, or at least act better. It's more useful, however, to help your partner feel entitled to these normal emotions and to feel safe about expressing them.

Validate yourself and your partner during times of intense emotions. Remind yourselves that intensity comes with the territory of this journey; it's part of how we humans process and adjust. You and your partner may need to educate friends and relatives who are worried about you.

Be aware that your feelings and expressions of those feelings toward each other may increase in intensity and this will require change and adjustment. Try not to evaluate what goes on now with the scale you used before. As you look at the situation, try to understand what is normal in these abnormal times. It is not only the negative feelings that will increase in intensity. You may find that the tenderness you feel for your loved ones moves you to tears, or the joy and appreciation of a sunrise feels overwhelming. All of life has increased intensity, and your emotions will reflect that.

If either of you has concern that there is any danger to self or others as a result of this intensity, talk with a professional counselor. It would be most helpful to seek out one who has experience in dealing with situations of life-threatening illness and loss. This professional needs to be one who understands the intensity and dynamics of such a situation.

TOOL TWO: AWARENESS OF STYLE

The differences in style between two persons in a committed, loving relationship form the basis of our conflicts and our attractions. These differences and how to live with them form a common theme for conversations, jokes, books on marriage, and workshops for couples. You and your spouse may have characterized yourselves as like "oil and water" or like "two peas in a pod," depending on how apparent your style differences are.

Style differences are the result of many different forces and events that shape us. Some of these are inborn. A significant part of our personalities is biologically based. Some of us are introverts, some extroverts, some passive, others active, some easily moved to emotional intensity, others more level and steady. Culture, values, and the constellation of our families of origin shape us. Our life experiences also influence who we are. Our gender comes with typical patterns of action and reaction.

Being in a committed relationship requires us to be constantly involved in compromising, accepting, changing, coping, stretching, rejecting, allowing, and moving toward or away from the differences of our partner.

When a couple faces cancer, these differences often take on a new intensity. The situation is defined in a non-negotiable way by an outside force — the cancer. One person is defined as the patient, and by default the other is not.

When Bruce was diagnosed with cancer, he was upset but did not express his emotions and preferred not to talk about it. His wife, Carol, cried a lot and wanted to talk about and process every aspect of the situation. Bruce was uncomfortable with the strong display of emotions by Carol, and was even worried that she was breaking down. Carol was concerned that Bruce was not dealing with the situation and would be harmed by stifling his emotions.

Tom, an active extrovert, wanted Judy to join support groups, do research, and get second opinions after she was diagnosed with cancer. Judy preferred to follow meditative practices and place her trust in her primary doctor.

After she was diagnosed, Barbara chose to decline aggressive medical techniques and follow a course of holistic and spiritual treatments. Greg, her spouse, desperately wanted her to engage in the treatments that would most aggressively attack her cancer.

When facing cancer, a couple's style differences take on the weight of the resulting actions, with possible life-or-death consequences. It's not always easy to look the other way and allow your spouse to just do it his or her way, especially if you believe that your way might save his or her life.

Also, because of the intimacy of the relationship, the actions of one have consequences for the other. If one spouse's style is not to talk, the other does not have a life partner to talk with during this frightening time. If one decides to quit work and live in the moment, the other loses an accustomed lifestyle.

Couples first need to be aware of and respect each other's style and needs. Second, the couple needs to talk about what will accommodate and meet the needs of both, as well as the relationship. This will require calm, patience, and talking time in the midst of what might feel like a howling hurricane blowing around you. Although we would like to believe that there is one sure plan of action we can count on to keep us safe from this cancer, there is not one way. The greatest probability for happiness in the present and a united strength against cancer comes from being centered and grounded in our individual styles with a plan for respecting and valuing the partnership. Talking, listening, observing, and discussing are the tools needed to accomplish this. Awareness of style differences requires nonjudgmental understanding of your partner's life view and behaviors. If you are too emotional or otherwise unable to have these conversations by yourselves, a counselor can act as a valuable facilitator to assist you in having productive discussions.

It is also very likely that you will receive lots of advice, ideas, and information from friends and family who care about you. Sometimes this can feel overwhelming. Remember, they are likely giving you advice that would fit with their own styles, which may or may not be yours. As you receive this information, accept it as the gift of love that it is, then continue to reflect on whether it feels right for your own style and that of your spouse.

TOOL THREE: SELF-CARE

Self-Care is recommended for the spouse, the patient and the relationship.

The Spouse

Often, the spouse is the one most neglected when it comes to self-care. The patient, by virtue of all the medical and emotional attention, may be very well cared for, educated, and supported in the necessity of taking care of self in order to achieve the greatest health benefits possible.

The spouse, on the other hand, may move quickly into a caregiver role out of necessity or a sense of duty and love.

This may be manifested by taking on the majority of household chores, increasing parenting tasks and responsibilities, taking on primary wage earning, acting as the spokesperson for caring friends and relatives, participating in treatment tasks and responsibilities, and acting as support person for the patient. The volume and intensity of these additional duties will ebb and flow with the course of treatment, the course of the disease, and the needs of the patient.

The caregiver tasks may be dictated out of actual necessity. They may also be a result of the spouse's desire to show love for the patient, a sense of need to "do something," and an unconscious response to preprogrammed expectations of what the spouse's role should be.

Thoughtful self-care throughout this journey is a must. It needs to evolve with the situation. If you, the spouse, become ill yourself or burned out, the result will be more challenges — and harder ones.

Geri solved the challenge of maintaining their rural home by allowing a team of friends and neighbors to set up a rotating chore list. This was difficult for the fiercely independent couple to do, but it allowed Geri and Paul to have quality time together.

Beth and Larry worked out a compromise by which she would join him in some activities and opt out of others. That way, she had time for her own hobbies and her developing career.

Carol stuck to a regular exercise schedule, which

provided a foundation for physical and emotional health. Bruce gave encouragement and support for time spent this way. To make time for exercise, the couple reevaluated priorities for household tasks.

Each of these couples found they had to get pretty stressed out and overwhelmed before realizing that a change was needed. The reality is that spouses do not acquire super-human abilities when their partners get cancer. The spouse needs TLC (tender loving care) to take on the challenges of being the partner of a cancer patient.

The Patient

The patient generally has the advantage over the spouse in terms of support for self-care. The medical team, family, and friends will find ways to be sure that injections are taken, or white blood cell counts are determined, or radiation is administered. The course of treatment gets defined, and all those involved gather with the patient to ensure those treatment interventions are accomplished. It is fortunate that it works this way for most patients, because the patient is often so impacted physically and mentally by the treatment itself that it can be difficult for the patient to remember to stay with the treatment protocol. For some patients, it is even difficult to get to the locations providing such treatment or to a pharmacy to obtain needed medications. It may be hard to make phone calls to arrange for these services or to deal with the volume of insurance correspondence now arriving at their homes. A network of providers and supporters helps accomplish a very important part of the patient's self-care.

Another level of patient self-care is sometimes not so clearly defined or accomplished, however. It involves the patient acting in ways that reflect either diminished capabilities as a result of cancer treatment or different physiological, emotional, spiritual, or relationship needs. For most cancer patients, the impact of treatment is profound on these life areas. Additionally, most people, cancer patients included, have a strong sense of independence and self-reliance. This admirable quality can hinder cancer patients from doing what needs to be done for themselves in new ways. Pride becomes a barrier to following good self-care practices.

Paul struggled longer than he should have to chop and cut firewood to heat his family's mountain home. This was his chore when he was healthy, and his pride made it difficult to let it go and consent to having his wife, sons, and neighbors take care of the firewood. Paul used up valuable but dwindling energy reserves by persisting in this task.

It is difficult for many patients to yield to the reality that they no longer have the energy, strength, or stamina that was available prior to cancer. This can also become a barrier to self-care by the patient.

Marilyn had just begun cancer treatment and intended to continue business and personal life as usual. She considered treatment time as off-work time that should not consume her energy; she also felt she was shirking her work responsibilities when undergoing treatment. Working full-time except for scheduled treatments and traveling out of state to help deal with a consuming family issue left her completely exhausted. Her exhaustion put her in a compromised physical condition, contributing to her difficulty in fighting a major infection that had invaded her body. Marilyn had "hit the wall" and concluded that she had to change something in order to recover. She shortened her workday significantly, made some adjustments to her diet, and started taking naps. She felt guilty about much of this, but she was so alarmed and surprised by her physical condition that she was willing to take steps toward self-care.

Much of the patient's self-care can be achieved simply through attitude adjustments that have acceptance at the core. When the patient surrenders to the reality that life is different, at least while in treatment, a sense of freedom is created that allows for many new ways of doing things. This also allows the patient to avoid the self-criticism that comes from insisting that he or she should still be able to do things in the same manner as in the past.

Bruce attempted to keep sharing the lawn mowing task with his wife, Carol, but found he was physically unable to do so. At that point, Carol took over all the mowing while Bruce stayed in the house and took naps in between guilty thoughts. When it became apparent that this was too much for Carol to handle by herself in addition to her spouse and caregiver activities, a person was hired to mow the lawn. Again, Bruce felt guilty and inadequate for not being able to carry this part of the chore load. He wanted things to be different, but reality would not yield. His physical condition pushed him into a level of self-care, essential to his recovery, that he had never before experienced.

As with spouses of cancer patients, the patients themselves need to be willing to ask for what they want or need. As a patient, you need to be willing to disregard some of the social rules; for example, when fatigued, sit down to talk to someone even though the other person may be standing. Be willing to go lie down even when visitors are in your home if that is the time you need for your nap. Be willing to sit in the car and wait while your spouse goes into the grocery store to shop, rather than dragging yourself up and down the grocery isles and needlessly spending energy. Be willing to say you need time to yourself and a break from supporters trying to keep you company. Be willing to speak so that others will know more clearly how to help.

The Relationship

Living in a committed relationship takes time, energy, and attention if that relationship is to stay vibrant and loving. Each stage in the development of a relationship comes with its own challenges. When cancer enters a household, the current challenges the couple is facing do not disappear. The stressors become additive. When a couple finds ways to meet these stressors as a team, in a loving way, the outcome is a closer, more intimate, more joyful way of living.

When a person gets cancer, it is most helpful for the couple to consider that facing the cancer is a team effort, a team project. The load is much lighter when carried together. Also, in reality, the relationship is facing cancer. All of the life interruptions, stresses, strains, fears, and frustrations will impact the relationship.

Jane and Walter had been married only a couple of years when Walter was diagnosed with cancer. While Walter's cancer was caught in the early stages and the prognosis was for complete recovery, the treatment to assure that it would not take hold again lasted over a year. Walter was fearful and the treatment made him feel ill much of the time. Jane didn't know how to respond to these changes. She said often, with tears in her eyes, "I want my partner back; I want the buddy I knew."

Paul and Geri had been married 20 years. They had found a comfortable pattern that allowed Paul to be not very communicative and Geri to attend primarily to parenting and maintaining the household. When Paul became seriously ill, this well-established pattern became unsatisfactory. Both felt the need to develop a more intimate way of talking. Geri realized she needed to learn to be more assertive and decisive about the business and decisions of the household, since her partner was less and less available to carry out his duties.

Beth and Larry found themselves frustrated by

competing needs: an intense desire to spend a lot of time together, in addition to personal needs such as their own hobbies and quiet time. As each reacted to the experience of cancer, they felt out of rhythm with each other. One of them would be in a phase of wanting lots of togetherness, while the other was feeling the need to have some space to sort things out.

Care of the relationship rests primarily on open, honest, loving talking about everything. Care of the relationship means finding or making the time for play and fun. When a cancer is in an active treatment phase, it can feel like it consumes your whole life. It's helpful to engage in activities that you used to do, if possible; if not, find new ones that bring joy and relaxation as a couple.

During Bruce's prolonged treatment, he and Carol could no longer do the hiking and camping they used to do . They found a craft class they could both take, to "play" together until Bruce's health returned.

Tom and Judy were not able to travel and be away from medical care for any length of time. Traveling and exploring new countries had been a passion for them. Instead, they explored local bed and breakfasts, to give themselves weekends away and satisfy their passion for seeing new places.

It is so easy to get caught up in activities required to treat the cancer and keep the household running that fun time gets lost. Here are some creative ideas that couples have developed:

• If you go to doctor appointments together, plan to stop for coffee or breakfast afterwards.

• Create a coupon booklet containing coupons that either spouse can present to the other, saying "I need time out" or "let's go play."

• Create romantic evenings with these rules: no talk of cancer and no problem solving.

• Accept offers from friends and relatives to take the kids for an afternoon or an evening. This also allows the helpers to feel less helpless.

• Spend "selfish" time alone, so that when you are together you have quality energy to give to each other.

• Join or start a group for couples, all of whom are facing cancer. It really helps to swap stories, ideas, and solutions. A support group provides a forum for both spouses and patients, where a spouse can vent about the challenges of living with a patient and a patient can talk about difficulties in the relationship from his or her perspective. In a context of support and caring, getting these things said while one's spouse in there to hear them leads to resolution, understanding, forgiveness, intimacy, and growth of the relationship. It helps to hear how other couples manage their situations. If no one has answers, it helps to sit together in understanding, encouragement, and support.

TOOL FOUR: RESHAPING THE RELATIONSHIP TO FIT THE SITUATION

Over the course of a marital lifetime, a couple must adapt their relationship to their current life stage and the life stage of the relationship. Generally a couple does things differently in a stage without children than when there are children in the household. A couple's activities usually change when they move from being a one-paycheck family to both earning a paycheck, and vice versa. Activities and ways of interacting evolve, based on the physical health and energy levels of a couple in their twenties versus a couple in their sixties.

If the couple, or one member of the couple, does not evolve, this lack of change will likely be a point of contention. For example, if income drops from two paychecks to one, and one partner is still spending as if there were two, conflict is likely to erupt. If a spouse is still carrying out the many activities enjoyed when there were no children, the partner may speak out to insist that activities change in order to share child care more fairly. These examples are logical, and with these types of life changes there is often so much advance warning and cultural modeling that the changes may occur without much need for discussion.

When a couple faces cancer, the lifestyle may need to change in a very short period of time and it may feel out of synch with how they would naturally be interacting. There may be no advance warning and no normal life models to emulate. Also, the couple may need to move in and out of changes depending on what phase the disease is in. It may feel as if they just accommodated and adapted to a new situation, only to have the situation change again, necessitating readjustment. When a patient is very ill from either the disease or the treatment, the spouse may move into a caregiver role. In this role, the spouse may need to administer treatment, provide medical support, and monitor the patient's activities to ensure safety. As soon as the patient gets better or the treatment ends, the spouse is no longer needed to hover over the patient and may even be told abruptly to back off.

When patients are in treatment such as chemotherapy or radiation, their energy levels may be much lower than normal even though they may look just as they did before. Couples may need to change the types of activities they engage in, or the length of time and the intensity. The night owl who would normally be able to talk until midnight may now fall asleep at 8:30.

One area that is often affected is the couple's sexuality. Because of treatment, a patient may be rendered impotent or unable to engage in sex due to pain or discomfort. Fear or exhaustion makes it difficult to feel romantic or sexy. However, when the situation changes and the patient feels well or the fear has passed, the couple may need to put energy into reinitiating their sexual activities. It would be a loss to the quality of the relationship to stay in the non-sexual mode which was only necessary because of treatment or illness issues.

When a person has been diagnosed with a life-threatening illness, it may be hard to relax and believe it when health returns. If a couple stays in the place of expecting loss or death after a patient has recovered, they may find themselves in a continually guarded way of living. They may miss opportunities for joy and adventure by holding back in fear, and thus miss the delights of a life fully lived.

It can also be the case that a patient cannot be cured and that there is no treatment that will keep the person alive. If partners avoid talking about the inevitable, falsely putting on happy faces or pretending that all will be well, they will create distance between themselves and lose intimacy. The challenge here is to learn how to talk and share in the reality of this stage of life, the time when the spouses know that one of them will die in the near future. The American culture worships life, youth, and vitality. Couples often experience difficulty in finding a role model or helper to assist them in building loving truth into this most important phase in the life of a couple.

For a couple facing cancer, these changes don't come as expected in the normal course of life. A young person in his or her twenties does not expect to be incapacitated or have energy too low to walk around the block. To evolve and adapt to these kinds of changes, the couple must focus on understanding what is changing and how they can create a new way of being in relationship.

Bruce and Carol enjoyed jogging together as a way to have fun and spend very special time together. When treatment robbed Bruce of energy, the couple walked. When more energy was lost, Carol jogged alone with feelings of sadness and loss. They were both surprised, when Bruce rejoined the activity after his treatment was over, that it took Carol a period of adjustment to welcome him back. The jogging time had become a precious private time for Carol.

Judy and Tom were not able to have sex while Judy was in treatment. The pain was too great and her body was too uncomfortable. They learned to express romantic love for each other in different ways. Giving each other pleasure and making each feel desirable took creativity and gentleness. When Judy was well again, they sought out the help of a counselor to overcome Tom's fear that he might hurt Judy and Judy's feeling of inadequacy as a partner.

Paul and Geri knew that Paul was going to die. All of the extraordinary treatment measures had been taken, so talking of health and cure no longer made sense. They took the leap of talking about how Geri might live her life after Paul's death. They shared together in their sorrow that she would be alone, and they gave each other courage in the present moment by being honest with each other about what they were facing. It meant different losses for each: for Paul, the loss of his life; and for Geri, the loss of the partner with whom she had chosen to spend her life.

These examples illustrate the importance of paying attention to the changes necessary to maintain a quality relationship throughout the journey of cancer. Likewise, a couple must evolve throughout the journey of normal life events to live fully and congruently within their current situation. Whenever a couple develops a way of being together that is not supported by the reality of present events, they will lose joy and quality.

TOOL FIVE: OPEN HONEST TALKING WITH YOURSELF (AND WITH EACH OTHER)

This tool may very well be the hardest to use. It is also the key to quality of life for the individuals and quality of intimacy for the couple. Receiving a diagnosis of cancer really challenges open, honest talking.

Open, honest talking with yourself means allowing all the thoughts that travel through your consciousness to be available for consideration with curiosity and acceptance. You may decide later that these thoughts are erroneous or not worth considering, but if you have considered them you can decide to toss them aside rather than just covering them up.

Perhaps your first thought after you hear your spouse has cancer is, "Maybe my partner will die." Then, you quickly cover it up by thinking, "Oh no, that's ridiculous negative thinking." As you put on a happy, positive face, your first thought has not gone away; it's just been stuck in a corner. Considering reality is not negative thinking. Cancer is a life threatening disease; however, depending on the type of cancer and when it is diagnosed, the probability of survival is very favorable. By being honest with yourself about the possibility of death, you can be open to hearing the real facts about the probability of life and health. Cancer can provide the opportunity to realize that life itself is terminal and we had better use it well. We can make changes if we have been wasting our time or living in a way that does not treat each day as precious.

Other thoughts a spouse might have include the following: "What about me? What will I do if I am left alone? What if my spouse gets really sick and needs a lot of care? Can I do that? What about my life?" These kinds of thoughts often trigger tremendous guilt. We catch ourselves and say internally, "What am I thinking? How can I be so selfish? My partner has cancer and here I am thinking about myself. This is ridiculous." It's not ridiculous. The quality and future of your life are just as important and precious and worth thinking about as that of the cancer patient. Give your concerns some thoughtful acceptance. Write them down, perhaps, in your journal, to be reviewed another day. As you learn more about the patient's condition and prognosis you can decide whether they are worth thinking through further or whether you can honestly say they do not need to occupy your time.

The patient's thoughts may reel to "I'm going to die. My life is over. Only terrible things are ahead of me." There is nothing defeatist or crazy about these thoughts. The truth is you may have some very tough times ahead, and you may die; but no one else has a life guarantee, either. With good medical care, good health habits, and a strong positive attitude, you may outlive many of your friends. You have been given a warning, and you can now take action. By honestly hearing yourself and your fears, you can make decisions about how to do the best you can to beat a negative outcome. If you don't allow yourself to consider such a reality, you may not work to full advantage to beat the cancer.

Another honesty challenge, if you are the patient, is to look at life and decide if you are living it with the highest quality possible. Are you spending your days building a life that fulfills your core values and beliefs? Are you living in a way that is true to yourself and your spouse, or are you acting out the expectations of others? It is seductive to think that you really just want to chuck it all and go live on a desert island; honest thinking may lead you to a different conclusion. You may find that accomplishing day-to-day tasks and being responsive to those you love can provide the highest quality of life anyone can attain. Reviewing and discussing quality of life issues with your spouse may be a very great challenge. We often live our lives on a conveyor belt consisting of what comes along next and what people expect of us. Cancer can challenge all that you have considered typical and normal, and along with it comes a challenge to your whole way of living.

It is possible for a bad marital relationship to become intolerable when the diagnosis of cancer comes to the door. Both spouses are faced with their own mortality and the quality of the time they have. It takes very honest thinking and talking to decide if the relationship can become healthy and rewarding through effort and counseling or whether it cannot.

Honest talking is so necessary for keeping a relationship vital and alive. However, honest talking can become a challenge when living with cancer. It is so natural for a spouse to not want to confront a patient or speak about his or her own anger and frustration; after all, the patient has cancer. When a spouse or patient chooses to not "bother" the other by communicating feelings, distance is created in the relationship. You may think you are protecting your spouse out of love and compassion, but constructive discussion or healthy arguing strengthens a relationship. Hiding feelings weakens the relationship and creates distance. This way of thinking and acting can seem quite opposite from natural inclinations. Perhaps you have gotten the message that a good marriage means people get along lovingly and cooperatively all the time and that when someone is sick, they should not be confronted with little day-to-day irritations. The fact is that, whether or not we are facing cancer, all humans still have down days, tired days, grumpy times, goofy days, indigestion, PMS, and headaches that impact how we act with our spouse and have nothing to do with cancer. The reality is that good marriages grow from working with differences, not ignoring them. If someone has the flu for a few days, irritations can be set aside. But cancer generally does not come and go in such a short period of time, and things that need to be talked about cannot wait until it goes away.

Patients may want to spare spouses from their fears and concerns. They may even feel embarrassed about how concerned and body-conscious they have become. It's not unusual to experience the feeling that your body has betrayed you by getting this cancer and now you can't trust it. By telling your spouse of your fears, he or she will better understand the reasons behind your actions or your quietness. The spouse will then need to decide if he or she can be the resource or support you desire. Through discussion and self-searching, the conclusion may be that you, the patient will find a counselor or support group for help in addition to what your spouse can offer. By making such a decision together, both patient and spouse can feel respected and loved.

When a spouse is in a primary caregiver role, it influences marital dynamics. A caregiver does not argue or expect intimacy from the patient. Couples need to talk about moving in and out of patient/caregiver roles as well as spouse roles. If the patient/caregiver times are temporary, couples can generally readily move back to their previous ways of being together. If the patient needs intensive caregiving for an extended period of time, the couple may need to talk about what is gained or lost or what needs to happen differently.

If the patient does move to a disease stage where there is no cure, the couple will find the greatest love, intimacy, and quality of life by being able to talk openly and honestly. This topic will be covered in detail in the chapter, "Destination: Death."

TOOL SIX: SEEKING AND RECEIVING SUPPORT

Oh, this is a tough one. We human beings are such an independent lot. We can handle it ourselves. We don't want to bother anyone. Privacy is so very important. Others will think I am not strong. Others will be repulsed. My friends have better things to think about. I don't like to be the center of attention. I don't like others to feel sorry for me. Nobody has the time. I don't like to talk about it. We go on and on, consciously or unconsciously, about why we don't open up to reach out to others, or let others reach out to us.

It is easy to find research that supports the premise that individuals that are in loving relationships live longer and are healthier than those who are not. In the cancer field, studies have shown that patients who are in a support group live longer than those who are not in a meaningful relationship. It is important, though, to find the kind of support that is most comfortable and meaningful for you. Some people receive all the support they need or want from one or two people; others thrive when they belong to several support groups and have a large network of friends. You and your spouse may have different thresholds for the right amount, type, and frequency of interactions with support people.

When thinking about what might be needed beyond medical treatments and interventions, there are two kinds of help to consider: professional and non-professional.

Non-professional Support

The first and most intimate support person available to you is your spouse. Using the tools described in this chapter will enhance your relationship and allow your spouse to be supportive through all that occurs when you interact. Being supportive does not mean that you have to sit down and talk about cancer for hours on end. We gain support from knowing that our partner loves and cares about us, that they trust us, and that we are a team no matter what happens. This kind of a relationship grows through all the conversations and interactions we have. Trust grows in a variety of ways, from figuring out how the chores get accomplished to the tone of voice we use when saying good morning to each other. As you use the tools to enhance your relationship and have a more joyful way of being with the one you love, you will also be developing a mutual support team that faces cancer together.

> Geri felt alone, confused, and miserable when Paul bravely faced his cancer alone, "like a man." Paul, on his part, didn't want to burden her. "She's got enough to worry about with the kids," he said. As Paul learned to talk openly to Geri, she felt lighter and energized, rather than burdened, by the surge of love she felt and the strength of their bond. She felt that together they could face anything. Paul was surprised at how good it felt to be able to talk. His strength and manhood were not diminished, but rather enhanced, by this new quality in his relationship with Geri.

Friends and family often want to be as supportive as

possible to a couple facing cancer. Sometimes their caring can feel overwhelming; the individuals and the couple need time and quiet to understand what is happening to them and to adjust their lives. It is very important for the couple to stay in touch with what is helpful from others and what is not. The couple may need to educate these caring people about what they really want and need. It's tempting to accept any and all contacts and help so as not to hurt the feelings of others who care. In the long run, however, the caring can change from support to another burden. You can lovingly but firmly let others know what works for you.

Susan and her colleague, Laura, worked with a very close and caring team of co-workers. Coincidentally, both were diagnosed with cancer within a short time of each other. Susan let her co-workers know that she welcomed all calls and visits. Laura let the group know that she and her husband needed private time. Her co-workers sent her love, prayers, and notes, but gave the couple the privacy they requested.

Jane's parents actually moved closer to Jane and Walter to provide support and help with child care. Their help was invaluable, but when Jane's mom took to popping over unexpectedly, Jane and Walter found themselves hiding to pretend they weren't home. Jane found the courage to tell her mom that she must call before coming over. After an initial period of discomfort, all were much happier.

Being open to support from others does not require giving up your independence, privacy, or strength. It does require opening your heart while honoring your personal style and needs.

Professional Support

There are many individuals and agencies trained to provide assistance and support to individuals facing cancer. You may have never used a helping professional before, or you may have accessed them as a resource in dealing with other personal challenges. Cancer can provide a level of stress, fear, and challenge that is best met by using a team of resources, both professional and non-professional.

When Bruce's melanoma returned, the only treatment recommended was a very challenging, yearlong course of injections every other day. The couple knew that, for a whole year, Bruce would feel sick most of the time and would be emotionally as well as physically challenged. They put a plan in place that included an individual counselor for each, a counselor for the couple periodically, and a support group for couples. These resources allowed them to complete the year of treatment and meet the challenges presented to them, both individually and as a couple. The helping professionals danced and sang with friends and family at the joyous celebration that marked the end of the treatment.

TOOL SEVEN: SPIRITUALITY

For many individuals facing cancer and their spouses facing cancer with them, spirituality is the primary thing that provides the strength, direction, and meaning to do all the other things that have been and will be talked about in this book. Note that spirituality does not mean religiosity. To be spiritual, one does not necessarily need to belong to a religion, attend a church, or even pray in the commonly used sense of the word. To be spiritual is to have a connection to something larger than ourselves and the tangible, concrete world we live in.

Beth and Larry were very grateful for their lifelong participation and belief through the Catholic faith. They attended church regularly and gained much comfort and courage through their unshakable beliefs.

Tom, a recovering alcoholic and spouse of a patient, found his direction, comfort, and courage through the twelve-step program and a higher power which had guided him out of alcoholism several years before. He had learned to place his trust in this higher power and to live in love in the moment.

Carol, a spouse, railed against the unjust God who could have let this cancer happen. Her sense of betrayal by what had seemed to be a loving God resulted in a yearlong journey of thinking, reading, meditating and talking. Her open, honest and very human interaction with God resulted in a greater connection and deep relationship with a trustworthy cosmic power, or life force.

Paul, a patient, earnestly said he was not spiritual and never went to church. However, he talked soulfully about the times he and his dog went out into the hills. He related how, in nature, he felt a peace, understanding and comfort that seemed to envelop him. This was where he received the strength to face his illness.

Bruce, a patient, followed many of the practices of the Buddhist religious tradition. His meditation and accepting mindfulness gave him a way of being and understanding that provided peace and joy.

These examples portray but a sampling of the vast array of possible forms that spirituality can take. Research is providing more and more data supporting that spirituality helps individuals live longer and healthier than their medical counterparts without spirituality in their lives.

Partners do not need to follow the same spiritual path in order for their beliefs to provide strength, comfort, and direction to their relationship. Each does need to respect and value the path of the other. If partners follow different spiritual paths and yet can come together centered as individuals, grounded in their own beliefs, they will come together in love and strength as a couple.

TOOL EIGHT: LAUGHTER

Cancer is not funny, but life is. It may seem strange to talk about laughing regularly throughout this journey, but those who have traveled it will tell you it is one of the most powerful tools for the survival of yourself, your health, and your relationship. Laughing is good for the body and the soul. When so much of life feels out of control, as it does when cancer invades your household, you might as well laugh as cry over the day-to-day events of life. One of the things that living with cancer can teach you is the difference between what is really important and what isn't. Many cancer patients and their spouses look back and laugh at how upset they became by things they thought were important before they began dealing with cancer. From the perspective of living with cancer, they can see that those irritations were not life and death as they had seemed. Cancer is life and death.

When you laugh, you release powerful emotions and reduce stress. When a couple can laugh together, it joins them on an emotional level. Of course there are times for the couple to cry together, or be angry together at this demon that has invaded their life. But if they can also laugh together, they experience a measure of victory over how much cancer controls how they choose to live.

Carol had days of being cranky and irritable over all the change, stress, and loss that Bruce's cancer brought into their life. As a couple they could laugh about the idea that she did not become a saint the day he got cancer. Her "feet of clay" became a loving characteristic to laugh about.

Tom and Judy laughed about the argument they had that left them not speaking to each other. Neither one really decided not to talk; each just became determined that the other needed to begin the process and apologize first. When Judy received a glowing medical report, she was left squirming with eagerness to share her news with Tom, while sticking to her guns about wanting him to reach out to her first. A day later, they laughed at how silly that all seemed and realized that it really didn't matter in the bigger picture.

When a patient loses his or her hair because of chemotherapy, it is often a sad and traumatic time.

When Judy was in chemotherapy and lost her hair, many offers of assistance with child care were received from friends and family. When Judy had completed her chemotherapy, she and Tom laughed impishly at the idea that she should keep shaving her head so that others would feel sorry for her and continue offering to baby-sit their children.

Laughing at our foibles and day-to-day life helps us to lose the pressure of needing to be perfect and in control of everything. Laughing also opens us to truly feeling joy, love, and passion for life and for each other. Sometimes laughter is spontaneous and impulsive, and at other times it can be a decision. When the journey is really hard, it may be time to cry for a while. When you are ready, give a laugh a try; if it feels good, try it again and again until you are laughing as much as you are crying. Nourish yourself, your love, and your relationship with full doses of all of your emotions. You may be surprised at how many things can bring you together in laughter, when you decide they are ridiculous or silly rather than awful.

Don't be afraid to cry hard together; just don't forget to laugh hard together, too!

Activities: Chapter 2

1. Keep a Journal: If you are not already someone who journals, we recommend that you start one. A journal need not follow any special format, be written in any particular kind of notebook, or be added to on any formal schedule. Be sure not to be critical of anything you write; your journal is a place of total acceptance of what you write and how you write.

The purpose of a journal is to provide a private place to explore and record your feelings, observations, learnings, and experiences. It will serve you as a place of centering and understanding, as well as a place to deposit those words that are too difficult to say. It is a place to contain your feelings of exultation as well as despair, fear as well as courage, hopelessness as well as determination. You can profess your love and your anger or frustration at your partner. A journal will get these thoughts and feelings out of your overloaded heart and brain and out into a place where you can either leave them or do something about them.

Judy shops for attractive books with lined pages. She looks for journal books that feel inviting to her and uses pens of different colors that record the mood she needs to convey. Often her journal "writings" are drawings that express experiences beyond the written word. Barry grabs whatever loose paper is near when he decides to write, and any pen or pencil close by is put to use.

2. Make Time: Create (don't just wait for it to happen) some quiet, uninterrupted time for the two of you to sit, for at least thirty minutes each day. This should not be at the end of the day when you may be exhausted. Your tasks are:

a. To be together for this time with no one else present.

b. To share any parts of your journals that you may want to. There should be freedom and acceptance from your partner that perhaps nothing from the journal will be shared, or that something will be shared, and that whatever is shared or not shared is okay. It does not matter whether or not the journal content is shared. What is important is that both of you are very conscious during these thirty minutes that you are thinking and caring and writing from your hearts about self and other.

c. To tell your partner what you would like him or her to know about you at this point in your travels along the journey described in this chapter.

3. Use the Tools. Commit to using the ONE DAY AT A TIME cards located at the end of this chapter. Cut them out of the book or make copies for you and your spouse.

Your ONE DAY AT A TIME card contains the list of strategic tools that will keep you and your love relationship strong and vital. Cancer and its treatment are challenging and tiring. The use of these tools will provide the emotional nourishment you will need.

Tape a copy of the card on your refrigerator, on your bathroom mirror, on the dashboard of the car. Carry a copy of it in your daily organizer book. Put it anyplace that you will see it every day.

Read this card thoughtfully every day. Take extra time with it when you or your relationship is hurting.

Notice what idea or emotion comes to you as you consider each question. Do at least one thing each day in response to the area or areas that need attention and nourishment. This chapter, "Tools for the Journey," will give you ideas and guidelines on how to attend to each of these areas. You may take some specific action as a result of reading the card, or you may go about your regular daily tasks with a different attitude, focus, or expectation because you have taken time out for this assessment. Either response will provide gentle, healthy nourishment to give you strength and courage, along with increasing your capacity for love, joy and laughter.

ONE DAY AT A TIME

1. ACCEPT: Your feelings and reactions are truly yours.
Embrace them and learn from them **today.**

2. BE AWARE: What do you need **today?**
What does your spouse need **today?**

3. TAKE CARE: What can you do **today** to care for yourself?

4. RESHAPE: What can you change in your relationship **today?**

5. BE HONEST: What are you really feeling and experiencing **today?**

6. RECEIVE: Let someone support you **today.**

7. ALLOW: Let your spiritual source carry some of your burden **today.**

8. LAUGH: **Every day.**

ONE DAY AT A TIME

1. ACCEPT: Your feelings and reactions are truly yours.
Embrace them and learn from them **today.**

2. BE AWARE: What do you need **today?**
What does your spouse need **today?**

3. TAKE CARE: What can you do **today** to care for yourself?

4. RESHAPE: What can you change in your relationship **today?**

5. BE HONEST: What are you really feeling and experiencing **today?**

6. RECEIVE: Let someone support you **today.**

7. ALLOW: Let your spiritual source carry some of your burden **today.**

8. LAUGH: **Every day.**

CHAPTER 3

THE NEWS

The NEWS arrives bluntly and powerfully when it is about a diagnosis of cancer. For most, it arrives with the lab test results, generally after too many days of waiting in fear and anxiety. We hope, and pray, and wish, and try to will away the possibility that the tissue holds cancer. But the lab results are not influenced by this effort, and the word "malignant" is spoken by a medical professional. Your head begins to swim and a dizzy sensation waves through you. After spending days with life on hold waiting for lab results, you feel as if you're being hurled in a projectile traveling ninety miles per hour. Things are suddenly traveling too fast, and it feels impossible to slow them down.

The NEWS often provides the road signs that plunge us into the start of the journey. Things begin to happen very quickly for the cancer patient and the spouse, and in turn, for their relationship. There are some particular issues that are characteristic of this stage, and these will be described in this chapter.

THREAT OF LOSS

A cancer diagnosis can shatter the illusion that most couples carry, the illusion that they will live together forever or at least until the age of ninety-five. Then, they can both decide what to do next with their lives. This fantasy is comforting and seems to ward off fears about realities that actually exist. With the NEWS, it is extremely difficult to hold on to the illusion of invincibility, and the couple's sense of security is yanked out from under them. This brutal lesson can turn into a gift or a blessing, but generally not until the couple has traveled further on the journey. For now, the experience is shock and then outrage that this undeserved event could happen to them.

As we have become acquainted with more and more couples dealing with cancer, it has become apparent that all couples go through the same process, yet each has a unique experience of the journey's various stages.

Judy and Tom received the news of Judy's cancer diagnosis as a minimal event. They were told the cancer was of no concern and would be of no great consequence to their lives. As a result, the NEWS was only temporarily upsetting. Because it was not perceived as a threat of loss, it did not throw this couple into the distress that most couples experience.

PULL AWAY VERSUS CLING

When the NEWS arrives, for some couples there is a move toward greater closeness. It may not necessarily result in intimate conversations about cancer and life or death questions, but rather in finding ways of spending more time together. The shock of the NEWS generally is so great that it is difficult to hold intimate, deep heart, deep gut conver-

sations. Instead the couple may elect to do more things together than is typical for them, while managing their respective fears as best they can. Sometimes they are too
shocked and too fearful to speak these fears to one another. For some couples, this becomes a time of pretending together that there is no bogey man haunting them, even
though their time together is dampened by a dark cloud they
cannot seem to shake, no matter how cheerful they try to
act.

For other couples, the NEWS stimulates a move toward
less closeness and greater relationship distance. The partners begin to disengage from one another as a way of responding to the ramifications of the NEWS. Perhaps a cancer diagnosis touches the spouse's issues of mortality so
that it does not feel safe to stay intimately involved; the partner can no longer support an illusion of immortality. Or perhaps the spouse does not feel equipped emotionally, physically, or spiritually to survive an anticipated long and difficult
course of cancer treatment and all the overwhelming demands such a journey places on the spouse.

Or, the patient will shift toward a quality of life focus,
rather than quantity, and will make decisions about whether
staying in the relationship is actually contributing to or hin-
dering this way of living. This can lead to reconnecting with
a current spouse in deeper and more satisfying ways or to
a decision to end an unsatisfying or conflictual relationship.
It becomes apparent that life is likely to be too short to not
make a significant decision about the relationship, in one direction or the other.

BALANCE

When the NEWS lands on a couple, it always has an impact on their relationship. It challenges the usual balance the couple has developed and enjoyed, even if the relationship is new. Part of the balance issue is about how two people interact with each other when they know each other intimately.

Tom and Judy spoke about how they used to talk openly with each other about everything. Then, when Judy received the NEWS, Tom began holding back and became less open. He feared adding burdens to Judy, who was already trying to deal with something awfully big. Similarly, Judy began protecting Tom from her own fears and did not want to reveal how terrified she was. Judy felt that by showing strength and not appearing afraid, Tom would be able to cope more easily. This couple temporarily lost one of their relationship strengths because the balance in their relationship dynamics was thrown off. Without the openness, there was less closeness at a time when they needed closeness more than ever.

SO MUCH TO LEARN AND UNDERSTAND

Upon receiving the NEWS, the couple is bombarded with information, much of which concerns either terminology or cellular functions unfamiliar to most of us. As mentioned in the previous chapter, "Tools for the Journey," style differences influence each person's efforts toward resolving, changing, stabilizing, and coping. These style issues also influence how a couple responds to data bombardment.

For Walter and Jane, Walter's cancer diagnosis was a major shock, and both felt immobilized and terrified for weeks. Then, while Walter stayed in this dazed immobility, Jane began to move toward a TEAM RALLY stage, explained in the next chapter. With this renewed energy, she felt compelled to research Walter's type of cancer and its treatment. As she got into this, she became increasingly frustrated with Walter because he was not participating in this research effort and in fact did not even appear to be interested.

Most couples experience some level of discord over managing the overwhelming volume of data they are confronted with, particularly since some of the data is emotionally sensitive — for example, the mortality rates for one's particular type of cancer or treatment. As described above, style differences between partners can contribute to the challenge of dealing with this data flood. For some patients, the treatment process makes them weak enough, tired enough, or sick enough that it is impossible to participate in data gathering or data interpreting. For this reason, many couples rely on friends or family to do their searching on the Internet, for example, and to sort through the information for relevant data. It is all right to rely on others to help you. The people that care about you want to do something to help; they are less fatigued than you and in a clearer head space to be able to do such research. Let them care about you!

CULTURAL AVOIDANCE OF ILLNESS

The word "cancer" makes many people uncomfortable, and being around someone who has cancer also makes many people uncomfortable. As a result, cancer patients and spouses are likely to observe some of their friends distancing or avoiding them when the cancer diagnosis becomes public. It is certainly not out of disrespect that this occurs; rather, it is a result of fear or discomfort. Sometimes a friend just may not know what to say and so stays away. A friend may be terrified of his or her own death, making it too challenging to be around someone dealing with cancer. Some couples find that friends and family ask only the spouse about how the patient is doing and never ask the patient directly.

The above experiences can have the effect of making the couple dealing with cancer feel isolated, unsupported, hurt, and angry. Patient and spouse may or may not experience this equally, particularly depending on who the offending party is. For example, pulling away by the spouse's father may not impact the patient the same way it does the spouse. Regardless of who feels the greater or lesser impact, these kinds of experiences can challenge the couple's relationship dynamics and push them off balance. Couples then have to decide what to do about any family or friends who are pulling away and, more importantly, what to do about each other's feelings so as to protect their own relationship.

Marilyn found that her mother avoided talking to

her about her cancer. This hurt Marilyn deeply, so she turned to her husband for empathy and advice. However, her husband had a long-standing conflictual relationship with Marilyn's mother. As a result, he felt tempted to advise Marilyn to do things that would get back at her mother and be hurtful to her. Fortunately, he was able to recognize this and acknowledge this to Marilyn, allowing him a way to stay supportive and caring with his wife. She understood his challenge with her mother and his commitment to objectiveness. This enabled her to speak openly and freely about her own frustrations and hurts without worrying about dealing with his reactions.

Activities: Chapter 3

1. Assess and Speak: Think about how your relationship is working now, particularly with the balance issues talked about earlier in this chapter. Review this not from a critical eye, but rather from an eye of observation. Consider if there are any ways in which your relationship with your partner has shifted away from the way you typically interact. For example, if your partner is not talking about his or her fears and is trying to ignore cancer's presence in your lives, consider bringing up the subject. Consider discussing it without the expectation that it needs to be different right now and without the impression that either of you is being criticized. If out-of-balance situations are happening in your relationship, remember that this is normal and does not represent a flaw in either of you.

NOTES

Patient notes: What's different in our relationship?

Spouse notes: What's different in our relationship?

Patient notes: What's the same in our relationship?

Spouse notes: What's the same in our relationship?

2. Journal: Continue the writing that you may have started in Chapter Two; if you have not started yet, go ahead and do so. At this point it is particularly important that you write the very things that might be too difficult to acknowledge to your partner or even to yourself. For example, writing that you are too terrified to think, talk or write about what cancer means to you is actually an important part of your own healing and recovery from this NEWS stage. It may feel silly to write in your journal what you are not going to write about, but it does make a difference in the healing process. You are now being strongly encouraged to put pen to paper and just do it. Do not think about proper words or spelling or grammar. Do not worry about writing complete sentences. Do write something, whether it be several half or incomplete sentences, a small list of words that are not in sentence form, or many words and sentences.

CHAPTER 4

TEAM RALLY

After the NEWS has settled in, couples often move into a very active high-energy time which we call TEAM RALLY. It is a time of intense activity in the effort of rallying against the cancer. Couples may move into TEAM RALLY within a matter of days after the NEWS. TEAM RALLY is often initiated with the advent of treatment activity. Often a surgery is scheduled within a matter of days, or the patient is recommended to meet with a series of specialists, all of whom will contribute their expertise and intervention to provide the most appropriate medical response in the shortest amount of time.

The TEAM RALLY can be a wonderfully loving and rewarding time even in the midst of fear and danger that seem to be swirling around the couple. It is a time of pulling together and acting as a single unit. Couples may express their love and concern for each other through caring actions and words of love not spoken quite so intensely in a long time.

The couple may feel very close and bonded. Cancer has become the common enemy and the petty irritations of day-to-day life get swept aside by the intensity of emotions and activities that are occurring. During this time, the patient may begin treatment. Many of the treatment modalities for cancer are intensive and time-consuming, dramatically compromising the patient's physical and emotional resilience. Typically the treatments consist of surgery, radiation, or chemotherapy, reaching for the most hard-hitting, effective intervention possible. Cancer is not a disease that allows for a soft or subtle approach. The disease is aggressive, so the treatment must be aggressive, also. As the couple bonds together to form a team, the hope is that they will be able to eradicate this thing from their lives and get back to regular life.

Joan, a spouse whose husband was moved quickly into very intensive treatment, was handling all the parenting, finances, and medical support, as well as juggling everyone's schedules. She burst into tears one day and cried, "This is not my life! I want my real life back. My real life is happy and orderly. We all work hard in our family and accomplish good things, our careers are fulfilling, and we are there for all our children's activities."

The issues of this TEAM RALLY stage are as follows:

EMOTIONS

During TEAM RALLY, couples often band together in a fear-driven yet optimistically determined way. For the couple, losing is not an option. This cancer is a foe, a threat to their home that their love and intense protective response actions will surely overcome. As a team, they are sure that if they do all they can and follow all the medical advice, the cancer will be gone as quickly and as surely as it came.

Some couples report intense emotionality, feeling greater love and loyalty than they ever experienced before. Others talk about moving into a numb autopilot state of just doing, doing, doing. Both of these responses burn up high amounts of energy.

ACTIVITY

The reality for the couple is that schedules need to be changed, child care arranged, insurance information researched, friends and relatives informed, chores rearranged, and work tasks postponed or delegated. This process of rearranging a family and home life at a moment's notice often takes the team, the couple, working together to plan and get everything accomplished. Medical appointments take up enormous amounts of time and are arranged to meet the already-full schedules of the medical facilities. Cancer requires that the couple drop all their other life priorities and attend to whatever it takes to halt the cancer.

During TEAM RALLY, the spouse is likely to become "super spouse." The spouse is the one to pick up all the slack. The couple had routines and ways to share chores and activities that the patient may now be unable to do. The spouse may also want to ease the burdens of the patient so that he or she can concentrate on getting well.

In addition to rearranging their normal activities and responding to the medical requirements, couples may add new activities to enhance their physical, emotional, and spiritual resilience.

Judy and Tom began to actively research Judy's type of cancer and how to best fight it. This included many hours on the Internet, learning about diet changes, and developing alternative health activities to build her immune system. They also participated in the traditional medical procedures.

Tammy and Jack took time during the two weeks before Jack's scheduled surgery to get away and relax, have massages, and practice positive thinking and imaging. These activities were undertaken as a team, but the purpose was to enhance Jack's likelihood of a successful surgery, by allowing him to be as rested, positive, and strong as possible.

GETTING TIRED

Given that the TEAM RALLY time on this journey is one of such high emotional and physical energy output, getting tired is a typical outcome. Often during this time, couples do not use the Tools for the Journey well. They are so busy and focused on doing all that needs to be done and facing the cancer that the relationship gets ignored. This is ironic, because of the strong experience of being a team during this stage. The couple is likely to be acting from a team stance, but not taking the time to build and maintain themselves and their relationship; there are just too many immediate demands.

If the cancer is eradicated by the initial medical intervention and the couple quickly returns to their regular lifestyle, they may feel a sense of good exhaustion. The elated feeling is that of a battle well fought. They experience the strength and vitality that they have as a team and a couple. They can be proud of how they worked together and grateful to each other for their contributions.

If the cancer does not respond to treatment, or if the treatment is long and arduous, TEAM RALLY can flow over into MARATHON. The couple may not realize it until they find themselves quite exhausted. The pacing and energy that it takes to run a sprint is vastly different from that which is needed to complete a marathon. A patient may not be able to continue with long-term treatment and keep up with regular activities. A spouse may not be able to keep doing double duty. MARATHON requires readjusting how things get done, rather than relying on the superhuman exertion of extra energy. The aspects of MARATHON will be described in Chapter Five.

When Walter's treatment first started, Jane really dug in to keep the household running smoothly. She did all her own tasks, plus carting the kids around, mowing the lawn, and doing chores that were typically Walter's tasks. They both felt good about how they were handling things and working together. After several weeks, however, Jane was exhausted and felt overburdened. It was time for the couple to rethink how they would get things done over the long haul that his treatment would need.

WHEN A COUPLE IS NOT A TEAM

There are situations when a couple does not move into TEAM RALLY. There seem to be two causes for this. The first is that a couple experienced such marital conflict before the diagnosis that they cannot join together, and the second is that one of the individuals is so overwhelmed or distressed by the situation that he or she is unable to act in tandem with another person.

Previous Conflict

Not all marriages are positive partnerships. Some couples have been living in conflict for many years. They may have learned how to live independent lives while still being married, they may be engaged in a relationship of ongoing declared conflict, or they may have been considering divorce at the time of the diagnosis. In these types of situations it may be impossible to join together because there is nothing left of the relationship. Or, it may feel dangerous to be vulnerable to this partner, since the relationship has consisted of disappointment, hurt, and disillusionment.

In such a situation, each individual is left to deal with the impact of the diagnosis on his or her own. Both may be impacted by an acute understanding of how much is missing in the relationship or how much has been lost in the marriage. Each may feel confronted by a realization of mortality and questions about the quality of life with this other person. Outwardly the couple may look like they are in TEAM RALLY because of the high level of activity and necessity to divide chores differently. What is missing is the invisible bond of partnership, of being together in love.

Charlotte had been in counseling to deal with concerns she had over the lack of a loving relationship in her marriage of many years. She had decided to ask her husband for a divorce and had worked out a plan of how she would make it on her own. Then she was diagnosed with cancer. She found she had to cancel her plans because she was reliant on her husband's insurance. She felt bitter and frustrated at this twist of fate and proceeded with treatment from a lonely, angry position.

If a couple is able, the diagnosis can move them to take action about the negative aspects of their relationship. The TEAM RALLY stage is often a catalyst for change to take place. NEWS is shocking and brief, but when there is a need to confront exactly how everyday life will be changed and what will be required of the individuals, the picture of the dysfunctional relationship becomes enlarged. Eventually, the problems of the relationship cannot be ignored.

George and Pat had survived many challenges in their relationship, but they remained bitter and distrustful of each other because of the dynamics established during difficult times. They often belittled each other, engaging in sarcasm and put-downs. They had participated in marital counseling but were unable to make the changes needed to live happily together. Pat's cancer diagnosis led them to counseling again. This time they were able to make changes, learn to accept each other again, and move forward in a respectful, loving way.

Steve and Cindy had a long marriage filled with conflict and antagonism. They had engaged in much marital counseling and several trial separations. After Steve's cancer diagnosis and initial round of treatment, Steve and Cindy were able to jointly decide that the best outcome for both would be divorce. They realized that they would not live forever, and they were no longer willing to live a life of conflict and unhappiness. Thus, while the cancer didn't cause the divorce, it spurred them to take action they had not previously been able to take.

Overwhelming Distress

Sometimes, patients or spouses can be so overwhelmed by the diagnosis that they are not able to join together in TEAM RALLY. They may become emotionally frozen in time, locked in their own emotional world.

Walter became so fearful about his diagnosis that he was unable to join with Judy in her efforts to think positively and plan life changes to support his course of treatment. As Walter continued to take no action while expressing his fear and anger, Judy acted as a cheerleader, started necessary projects, and made all the appointments. When Walter didn't soon join her, she tired out and felt resentful. Walter eventually moved out of the overwhelming fear in which he had been mired, but by that time the treatment had been under way for quite a while and they were into the MARATHON stage. Judy was glad he was changing, but she continued to feel as if they were on two different paths.

SUMMARY

TEAM RALLY often happens automatically and is orchestrated by the events of the situation. Couples may feel that it is just the normal, expected way that any couple would react. However, the way a couple responds to the situation can be a reflection of the state of the relationship. The TEAM RALLY stage of the journey also provides an opportunity for intense bonding and a commitment that the couple is in this together. What the individuals learn about each other in this early stage of responding as a team to cancer sets the foundation for how the couple will weather the challenges ahead. If both individuals feel trust and intensity of commitment from their partners at the beginning of a challenging time, they may rely on that throughout the journey. It will help each one to have confidence in how the other responds and reacts to this type of challenge, which is likely different from anything the couple has faced before in their marriage.

TEAM RALLY does not just happen one time along the road of cancer. Couples will likely move into TEAM RALLY many times over the course of the treatment and the illness. Whenever there is a crisis, a new challenge, a necessity to react and regroup in the face of difficult news, there is the opportunity to move into TEAM RALLY. It is the act of joining together positively and intensely to team up against a new challenge.

Activities: Chapter 4

1. Appreciate: Sit together, as a couple, and list all the things that each is doing to support this time of life, facing cancer. If you don't have time to sit together and discuss, talk about it while you are driving in the car, doing the dishes together, or putting the kids to bed. Acknowledge and appreciate each and every piece. Don't forget the little things. Each small act of kindness, appreciation, encouragement, and support is a building block. One brick may not seem like much, but piling them all up builds a strong wall able to withstand the forces of great winds. The cement is the love and caring.

NOTES

Patient notes: What am I doing and what is my spouse doing to support this time of life?

Spouse notes: What am I doing and what is my spouse doing to support this time of life?

2. Find Balance: Now consider what activities can be given up or delegated to others. Consider what feelings accompany all of this activity. Talk openly about any feelings either of you might have such as guilt, helplessness, resentfulness, or being overwhelmed. You may not be able to change much about the actual current situation, but talking about the experience will bond you as a couple and relieve the burden of carrying around negative feelings by yourself.

NOTES

Patient notes:

Spouse notes:

3. Discuss Needs: Finally, check in with each other. See if there are additional things that either person needs or wants. Perhaps one of you really would like more hugs, or more time alone, or time out as a couple. Be sure to attend to the needs of both spouse and patient. To complete the journey, each member of the team must be cared for and stay healthy.

NOTES

Patient notes: I need. I would like more of ...

Spouse notes: I need. I would like more of ...

CHAPTER 5

MARATHON
AND SLEDGEHAMMERS

Once the NEWS has arrived and partners have had time to accommodate both the concept that cancer is with them and the concept of a prescribed, planned course of treatment, couples generally move into the TEAM RALLY stage described in the previous chapter. One of the primary contrasts between this phase and the current one of MARATHON AND SLEDGEHAMMERS is that the highly energized rally shifts to a steadier, more even energy level that is often quieter than in the rallying moments. There is a sense of settling in for the journey, at least for as much of it as can be predicted at this point. Couples experience a kind of commitment to the treatment of cancer and a commitment to whatever the journey entails.

At this point in the journey, most couples have been rearranging their life and work patterns to accommodate the dozens of medical appointments, exams, follow-up exams, additional surgical procedures, chemo treatments, radiation treatments, injections, infusions, blood tests, X-rays, CAT scans, sonograms, MRIs, and trips to pharmacies to gather expensive pills. It is as if the cancer treatment has taken over and the rest of life has to fit in where it can. Perhaps this means the patient reduces, flexes, or quits work and home responsibilities. Perhaps it means the spouse and patient reduce their involvement in social or community activities. Couples adjust schedules and expectations so that naps can be taken during the day and nothing is planned during the predictable nausea following certain treatments.

Instead of coming as surprises, as when first beginning treatment, these treatment impacts are now known and become a part of the new schedule, a part of the new, predictable routine. Each couple finds a way to make the medical treatment and the conquest of cancer the highest priority and to reprioritize other life and work activities in a new way. As this is done, a routine evolves for the couple, family, and workplace that is different from previous routines; nevertheless, it is a routine. We each seek such patterns throughout life, and just because cancer is visiting does not mean we no longer need or seek the comfort of familiar ground. It helps us reduce the sense of chaos and the feeling of loss of control. Most of us find some level of comfort in knowing what is ahead and our routines seem to help us in this way.

MARATHON

Successful completion of the MARATHON stage requires attention to several areas such as:

Stamina and Pacing

It is impossible to know the duration of treatment and the path of the cancer at this point. Even so, there is generally a sense that this is going to be a long journey, one that requires pacing and conservation of energy. The couple must develop a patient persistence about enduring the treatment phase in order to eradicate the cancer.

Bruce had completed surgery, the removal of lymph nodes that were malignant melanoma, and was beginning a course of treatment that was to last twelve months. There were to be infusions every weekday for a month, then injections every other day for the remaining eleven months. The chemotherapy created a constant, daily experience of body pain, profound fatigue, nighttime chills following each treatment, and numerous other side effects that greatly impacted his quality of life. In addition, there were three office visits a week for treatments and one or two visits a week for blood tests, plus several hours each afternoon that Bruce needed to sleep to help deal with the fatigue.

There were two things that happened at this point. One is that the treatment issues took over his daily schedule, and the rest of life had to find a way to occupy whatever was left over. In this regard, a new routine began to form, and before long this new routine was the old habit. A certain comfort developed with the routine, and less concentration was required over time to be sure appointments were not missed.

The second thing that occurred is that Bruce felt

overwhelmed with what he perceived to be an impossibly huge task of completing such a long treatment regime. Mentally, it was too much for him to imagine twelve months of chemotherapy side effects, so the process did not seem doable. He had to chunk it down into more manageable segments. He and his spouse did so by focusing on getting through one week of treatment at a time; at the end of each week, they would do a small ritual to recognize that achievement. For them, this was the only way they could keep moving along on a path that seemed to have no end.

Normal Life Events

Such is the experience of the MARATHON for many couples. The task becomes figuring out how to meet the demands of treatment over a long span of time while continuing to live in the normal places. The rest of life continues to present itself while the patient and spouse are using energy, time, and money to meet the challenges of cancer treatment. Normal life events are not suspended during treatment. Children are still in school and continue facing homework, attendance, and social issues that parents become involved in; these don't wait until cancer treatment is over. The dog still needs attention from the veterinarian, the neighboring teenager still has parties late at night that wake you up, your parents' health may be suffering, the car still needs repairing, and so on. It was hard enough to keep up with all these things before cancer visited, and during cancer treatment they can feel a bit overwhelming. Open communication between patient and spouse becomes more essential than ever, since time and energy have become more limited than before. Priorities have to be examined; new resources are often needed; different ways of doing family business are often created.

Since this MARATHON stage generally lasts so long, the earlier, short-term solutions that might have worked in the NEWS or TEAM RALLY stages will no longer appear feasible. Systems are needed that can stand the duration of a lengthy treatment protocol. Given that the length of treatment is generally unknown, this can create some unique challenges to the decision-making process for a couple.

Larry was in his tenth year of cancer recurrences and treatments. Beth had just completed preparation to start a new career, a dream that had required tremendous effort and fortitude. Now she was faced with a decision about pursuing her dream career at this time or tabling this path in order to stay available and connected to Larry. It looked as if Larry might not survive this recurrence of cancer, yet there was a possibility that he could easily live another year or two. If the MARATHON were to last only a few months, this kind of decision would be much easier. There would be fewer consequences in setting aside Beth's career goals for a short time than if she waited several years. Larry and Beth had to do some very honest talking with each other in order to come to a decision that served them both. They spoke about life expectancies instead of pretending that Larry was unlikely to die soon. They talked about how they wanted to live these years together if they were the only years they had left as a couple. They spoke about what could happen to a person if a dream is set aside, the impact on that person's heart and spirit, and the subsequent impact on the couple's intimate relationship. Through many discussions about these things, they reached a solution that both could support.

Without such talking, the issue could have created a barrier to their close relationship, as it would for any couple. Unspoken issues are still filled with energy and always have an impact on a couple's relationship.

Sexual Intimacy

In addition to impacting other aspects of relationship intimacy, the MARATHON affects sexual intimacy. Surgery, chemotherapy, and their side effects, as well as issues about the physical body looking different, are just some of the challenges to a couple's sexual intimacy. Again, short-term solutions developed during the NEWS or TEAM RALLY portions of the journey may not represent how the couple wants life to work, but the partners generally accept this temporary disruption in their sexual relationship. The MARATHON, however, poses a different problem in that the challenge may go on for a long time. The decision during earlier phases may have been to suspend sexual activity temporarily, but the possibility of suspending it for what seems like forever will be unacceptable for many couples.

George's ongoing treatment began to impact his

sexual functioning by making erections difficult to achieve, shutting down his ability to climax, and significantly reducing his interest in having sex. For George and his spouse, their sexual intimacy was a haven, and now this was being taken away from them at a time when they especially needed a place to escape. There was a heavy sense of loss for this couple, and they needed to create a solution that would allow them to experience the greatest quality of life possible while enduring the effects of the ongoing treatment. Talking and crying together eventually brought them to a satisfactory way of maintaining their sexual intimacy in a new way. Without addressing this sensitive issue, other aspects of their relationship intimacy would likely have begun to erode.

It is important for couples to have information about how various cancer treatments are likely to affect the patient's sexual functioning. Unfortunately, many medical providers do not speak to this aspect of the proposed treatment, so couples may need to initiate such conversations with their oncologists or other medical team members. Hundreds of thousands of patients have been recipients of most cancer treatments, and much is known about the typical side effects, including those related to sexual functioning.

For example, it is common for people undergoing chemotherapy and radiation treatments to experience a diminished desire for sex. This can be due to the profound fatigue that often accompanies these treatments and to the impact of treatment on the hormone and endocrine systems that regulate the different aspects of our sexual functioning. These side effects tends to fluctuate for most patients, depending on proximity to the most recent treatment date and the intensity or dosage of that treatment.

If a couple is experiencing an impact on sexual functioning, it is helpful to consult a gynecologist, urologist, or other specialist to learn of available treatments and remedies. It may also be helpful for the couple to meet with a sex therapist for support in dealing with these sexual issues.

As the patient and the couple enter an active treatment phase, such as chemotherapy or radiation, they will begin to discover what is possible for them regarding their mutual sexual functioning. For example, the patient may learn that sexual activity is not possible for perhaps at least five days after a particular treatment (this varies and is highly individual), and after that time, sexual abilities are relatively close to that experienced prior to cancer treatment. The couple then is able to use this information to anticipate or plan ways they would like their sexual intimacy to work, given the known impact of the treatment. This particular couple may decide to suspend sexual intimacy until after the fifth day following treatment. They might also decide to modify their usual way of having sexual intimacy during the days closer to treatment by accommodating to the patient's diminished energy or desire.

Other couples will discover different patterns to the side effects of cancer or its treatment that impact sexual functioning. Some may find that the side effects of treatment are continuously experienced throughout the duration of treatment and that they must make a longer-term modification of their sexual practices. This involves open communication between spouse and patient as to what each needs within this new way of being sexual with each other. It also involves dealing with the sense of loss about sexual practices in which they can no longer engage.

Surgery creates its own challenges in the sexual arena. Physical soreness or pain following surgery can impair a patient's desire to have sex, and fear of increased body pain as a result of sexual activity can override desire for sex. Typically, recovery from these aspects of surgery is relatively fast, so the couple may decide to observe more extreme but temporary modification of their sexual practices, such as abstinence. Their intention might be to resume usual sexual functioning once the patient no longer experiences the pain or soreness resulting from surgery.

Surgery that changes body appearance, such as a mastectomy, creates a different type of impact on a couple's sexual intimacy. The patient's sense of attractiveness can be profoundly altered following such surgery. Sexual intimacy is about love, but it is also about feeling desirable to one's spouse. If the patient's body has scars, indentations, or no breast, a significant adjustment to body image and self image is required in order to resume sexual intimacy. Similarly, the spouse may also have adjustments to make. The possibilities for misunderstandings and hurt feelings are enormous during this time, and open, honest communicating becomes the means for keeping the couple's love alive.

Some couples deal with body image issues by gently and slowly moving to an acknowledgment of the body changes, while at the same time dealing with the anger and grief that accompany these physical alterations. When courage is sufficient, some couples incorporate a practice of uncovering these body areas for both to see. Then, they move toward patient and spouse both lovingly touching these areas and identifying these special places as symbolic evidence of the defeat of cancer or as evidence of the opportunity for life. This is certainly not an easy part of the couple's journey, and it must include ways to grieve and even rage against whatever losses have been experienced. Embracing the losses in this way is just as important as identifying the special body areas as evidence of healing intention.

Competing with cancer generally requires giving up certain things in order to gain something else, namely life. Because of surgically losing part of one's body or losing functioning capabilities due to other cancer treatment, the couple may have to alter their way of engaging in sexual intimacy. It is essential that patient and spouse find courage to speak openly to each other so that the sexual experiences and needs of each can be welcomed into the loving energy used with the other aspects of their journey with cancer.

As with all other stages in this journey with cancer, issues about sexual intimacy are about the couple, not just the patient. Decisions about sexual practices need to take into account the needs of patient and spouse. It is not unusual for a spouse to continue feeling a usual level of sexual desire, for example, even though the patient's desire has diminished. Or the spouse may continue being able to reach a climax even though the patient cannot. Capabilities, interests, and desires of both people need to be shared and discussed. Ignoring one person's needs in favor of the other can lead to a decision that will challenge the couple's relationship and sexual intimacy rather than supporting it.

Summary

The MARATHON is a journey that is about two people, not just the patient. The cancer and its treatment impact both partners. It is their relationship that is traveling on this journey. The Marathon presents an opportunity for a couple to create a stronger sense of relationship commitment and strength. Those couples who successfully complete this part of the journey receive one of the gifts of the cancer experience that can always be theirs, the gift of experiencing relationship intimacy very close to its deepest level.

SLEDGEHAMMERS

The couple has now been traveling along the Marathon journey of cancer treatment and experiencing all the accommodations that go along with it. It's not a path of choice, but the couple now knows what the journey is and what it entails. Unfortunately, for many couples, things do not stay the course and a surprise of one kind or another occurs during the MARATHON.

Marilyn and Mark had committed to Marilyn's

treatment protocol for the past eighteen months. They had gone through some very challenging times with medications that caused adverse side effects but had gotten those things straightened out. Her markers were looking better and better as treatment progressed, and she and her husband had moved into a hopeful optimism about her prognosis. Then cancer was discovered at a new site, and a sledgehammer landed on them. For Marilyn and Mark, this was very discouraging news, particularly after working so long and hard to beat the first cancer and survive the course of treatment. It also signaled a time of pulling back together again, to rally, to unite, and to gear up for the next battle with cancer. Their relationship had enjoyed the vacation from treatment; with chemo treatments suspended and Marilyn feeling so much better, they had settled into a more usual way of being with each other. Their household had begun to feel somewhat like it used to before cancer.

When a SLEDGEHAMMER occurs, things feel unsettled again and things feel frightening again. Depending on treatment decisions, the couple may be required to negotiate their role responsibilities again regarding household and family tasks, employment adjustments, and so on.

A SLEDGEHAMMER can also occur during ongoing treatment, with the same unsettling and fear-arousing effect. These events are alarming, and they shake whatever level of security the couple has been able to create. As a result, the relationship is often challenged. Coping mecha-

nisms are energized, and if styles are very different between patient and spouse, tension can develop within their
relationship. Each is trying to deal with the SLEDGEHAM-
MER and understand what it means in terms of duration
and quality of life. The couple may find it difficult to talk
about such frightening and painful issues. Not only are the
cancer survival issues at stake when these SLEDGEHAM-
MERS arrive, but other ramifications of treatment or non-
treatment will have to be reconciled.

Katie and Dave learned that if Katie received
treatment for her breast cancer, she would become
infertile and unable to conceive a second child. Having
more children had always been a part of their dream
and life plan, so they had a decision to make. Should
Katie forgo cancer treatment, meaning they would
take their chances with Katie's cancer while trying to
have another child, or should they increase Katie's
chances of survival and give up their dream of another child? They decided to give up their dream of having another child so that they would have a greater
chance of raising their three-year-old daughter together and spending more life together as a couple.
The decision, though, was made with much pain and
agony.

The relationship balance can easily be challenged in
these circumstances, in part because so much is usually at
stake with a SLEDGEHAMMER. There are a number of
strategic tools (see Chapter 2) that can be of great use to
the couple in dealing with SLEDGEHAMMERS. Of particu-

lar value are the tools of "Open Honest Talking" and "Reshaping the Relationship to Fit the Situation."

Talking

Open and honest talking will help the couple stay united in the face of difficult decision making. This prevents either the patient or the spouse from carrying the weight of such a decision alone. If two people can persist in talking openly, they will find a way to approach SLEDGEHAMMERS as a team and perhaps even strengthen their relationship further than could be imagined.

Judy and Tom had a strong and close relationship prior to Judy's cancer diagnosis. They were faced with the SLEDGEHAMMER of making a decision about the type of treatment to pursue following her surgery and chemotherapy. It appeared that the only treatment remaining was one that was relatively new. It had received mixed reviews about long-term side effects, including a significantly increased risk of a different type of cancer developing. The couple researched every possible angle on the new treatment and began trying to come to a decision that felt right to each of them. Early in this process, Tom had a different view from Judy's, yet found a way to be honest with her without making her feel she had to see the issue his way. Likewise, Judy was able to receive his input while staying honest with him about how she felt about the issue. Through loving patience with this process, they were able to come to agreement on the treatment

approach, and each continued feeling valued and respected by the other.

Relationship Accommodations

When a SLEDGEHAMMER occurs, reshaping the relationship generally involves a new adjustment in attitude or
behavior. Most couples feel they have already accommodated a great deal, and the new demands of the SLEDGE-
HAMMER can feel overwhelming. It is as if they have finally found the right setting on the cruise control after several
major adjustments in speed; now they have to look at
changing the cruise control setting again, and not in the direction they would like. Some couples wonder just how
much more they can take. Some couples find they have to
cross the line in the sand they swore they would never be
able to cross. Now they realize there may be no reasonable
alternative but to go ahead and cross that self-imposed line.
The line could be the use of a wheel chair or consenting to
have a body part surgically removed. As the patient and
spouse cross these lines together, their relationship evolves
to accommodate whatever changes such decisions bring.
Such a transition requires much patience, gentleness, and
loving compassion but can result in a strengthened partnership. If the couple is unable to evolve in this way, it is likely
their closeness and intimacy will be compromised, with a
sense of personal distance developing between them.

Activities: Chapter 5
For the Marathon:

1. Speak and Listen: Commit to talking to your partner about the specific impacts of this long-term phase on your relationship interactions and all aspects of your relationship intimacies. Share what this new challenge is like for you, and ask what it is like for your partner to experience this challenge. Listen with a loving, accepting mind that holds no judgment or criticism but instead holds interest, curiosity, and compassion. When both of you have thoroughly expressed and have been thoroughly heard, decide out loud if you are ready to proceed as a couple to create whatever you need in the way of solutions, new ways of doing things, and new expectations of self and other. Write these things down so you can use them as anchor points for future discussions and decisions.

NOTES

Patient notes:

Spouse notes:

2. Find Support: Consider finding and joining a support group for couples. This will give you the opportunity to speak about your journey with others who will understand immediately what you are describing. If no such groups are available in your community, consider asking for help in creating such a group from the support staff at your oncologist's office, a local cancer resource agency, your pastor, or other cancer patients and spouses; or, contact the Couples Facing Cancer program.

3. Evaluate Chores: Consider all household routines, tasks, and priorities. Decide together which ones should be done differently. Explore to see if there are chores that can be ignored, done less frequently, or hired out. If you are involved in community activities, you may need to take some time out. Job hours or commitments may need to be reduced.

NOTES

Patient notes:

Spouse notes:

For Sledgehammers:

1. Be Slower and Calmer: Try your best to slow things down, or get the help of others to slow things down and shed some of your responsibilities for the moment. You are likely to be facing an important decision about cancer treatment, and it is essential that you and your partner create the best climate possible to confront this new information. Considerations need to be given to resting, eating well even if not eating much, drinking lots of water, spending some time breathing the outdoors air, gently or vigorously moving about depending on what type of physical activity you like to do and are able to do, and any other wellness practice that you know helps you. If you need additional information or consultation with someone, decide what or who that is. Both of you need to do whatever it takes to obtain these things. Ask for help from friends and family if you need to, in order to accomplish the above. People want to help you but don't know how unless you extend an invitation. Don't be selfish; let other people into your lives. They have gifts for you, and you have the same for them.

NOTES

Patient notes: I need ...

Spouse notes: I need ...

2. Journal: Use your journaling to help quiet your mind as much as possible and to help understand more clearly the actual core issues involved in the decision you are facing. It is easy for our minds to get jumbled up when challenged with a SLEDGEHAMMER, and writing will often anchor those circling thoughts so your logic can begin to put the ideas into some sort of order.

CHAPTER 6

LIFE THREAT

There may be a time during the course of cancer treatment when the patient's life is acutely threatened. This LIFE THREAT is outside of the expected course of cancer; it may occur if the cancer does not respond to treatment. The life threat may actually come from any number of situations. It may even be a result of the aggressive treatment that is necessary to intervene in the course of cancer. If a cancer cannot be eradicated, there is often an expected path of illness and decline that a couple, while not totally adjusting and accepting, can understand and move through with some expectation of what might happen next. Individuals with fighting spirits and positive thinking can set their course toward health while having an understanding of what could happen if they are not successful. LIFE THREAT, as we define it, does not follow this natural course of events. In this situation, the threat comes out of the blue. It is unexpected and does not fit into the natural and expected course of a disease.

Bruce was in an aggressive, yearlong treatment program. He and his wife, Carol, had learned about the treatment and the challenges of the side effects; they had altered their lifestyle to support the program. Bruce had reduced his work schedule significantly, entered into a program of daily rest, changed diet, and reduced strenuous activity. The LIFE THREAT came when his blood chemistry responded to the treatment so dramatically that his own body became a threat to him. The couple had to choose whether to continue the aggressive treatment with its inherent risks or to back off and increase the risk of the cancer.

Larry was receiving very strong doses of a difficult chemotherapy. He and Beth had accepted how challenging the process would be. They arranged for additional health care professionals to assist them in managing what they anticipated to be a difficult time. What they weren't prepared for was Larry's liver reacting to the chemotherapy in such a way that emergency measures were necessary to save his life.

Susan had been following a program of very aggressive treatment. Her cancer was tough and invasive. She and Vic courageously chose treatment procedures that caused both to sacrifice and make many changes. They had just completed a successful round of treatment that gave them much hope and excitement about the future. During a summary checkup, a new, large tumor was found that had been previously undetected and was an immediate life threat.

Often in a LIFE THREAT situation, the couple moves quickly into very divided patient and caregiver roles. The patient may feel very sick and frightened, and the spouse may need to take charge of the physical events that need to happen to keep the patient safe. The couple may feel the same challenges inherent in the experiences of NEWS and TEAM RALLY. In essence, this is what occurs; this is how the journey with cancer works. Places we have visited along the journey are revisited. This is not a journey down a straight road to a known destination. It is one of revisiting, reacting, adjusting, and setting out again. The couple takes on the experience of LIFE THREAT, which is NEWS of shocking and devastating impact. The partners must then go through the processes necessary to balance, adjust roles and actions, and continue traveling.

A LIFE THREAT often brings friends and family closer. That may mean more intense expressions of love, caring, and concern and more actual contact and interaction with them. You may need their assistance for a while to complete all the tasks to be done. Such closeness and intensity, while likely welcome and needed, will require adaptation by the patient and spouse in terms of how their relationship is impacted. Using the strategic tools will assist the couple in staying centered and healthy during this stressful time. The tools will also help them when the crisis has passed, as they move back into roles and routines which are the healthiest and most comfortable for them in the long-term picture.

Couples make many changes when responding to an acute crisis situation; they make changes once again to return to normal living. Couples often describe this as a roller coaster ride. They find these changes challenging and draining and learn that the strategic tools are necessary to maintain energy and health as individuals and as a couple.

LIFE THREAT situations can seem like a betrayal, an insult, an intrusion. They often occur when the couple is doing all the right things, following what is recommended to save the patient's life, working with the reality of their situation, and believe that they have already accepted some of the hardest things life has to offer. LIFE THREAT is an imminent and unexpected danger to the patient's life; it is the ultimate SLEDGEHAMMER for the couple that is focusing on what it takes to run the difficult MARATHON that promises to eradicate this dread cancer that has invaded.

It is so easy and natural for us humans to believe that we are in control and that, if we do the right things, we will be safe. Cancer shakes that comfortable notion of safety. But even when we accept that we are not immortal, we can quickly move into the belief that, if we just follow the treatment prescribed, we will again be safe. LIFE THREAT once more wipes out that comfort zone. The threat of loss is gripping and powerful; it can feel as if there are no rules and there is no safe place.

Given all the negative aspects of such an event, it can feel preposterous to a couple to believe there is a gift inherent within the situation. The gift is the ultimate lesson that the only time a couple can count on is the present. The challenge is to make each day, each minute, each hour of the highest quality. It is not about living in fear, because that results in losing the quality and joy of the time you do have. It is about living in the reality that there are no rules and there is no way to live that will guarantee safety. If you follow all the treatment recommendations and live in a healthy way, what you are doing is raising the probability that you will live long and be healthy. It's not unusual to fall into thinking that if you follow treatment and live right, you should live long and be healthy. The amazing outcome that is often seen in couples that are living through such a difficult time, or have lived through it, is that they are joyful, loving, and freely living life to the fullest. They are not living in the complacency of taking their spouses and their daily life for granted.

LIFE THREAT is one of the worst of all situations, with the potential for the most valuable of all lessons. In the midst of the situation, the couple does not know what the outcome will be, whether the patient will live or die. When the patient does recover and live, the couple has another chance to live and love in a way perhaps not available to them before. Each can come away with a new understanding of the miracle of being alive and living with a chosen life partner.

Activities: Chapter 6

1. Notice: Each morning couples get up, rushing or dragging through the daily chores of getting the household awake and moving for the day. Usually we are keeping an eye on the clock, planning the management of the day's activities, and unconsciously completing the necessary tasks.

Build into your routine (perhaps while you are brushing

your teeth) the opportunity to think of one thing that your spouse brings into your life that you are grateful for. It doesn't have to be major, or poetic, or deeply intense, just a quick thought of one thing. If the two of you are fighting, or if you are irritated with him or her, it may feel difficult or like a betrayal of your point of view to think kind thoughts. But such an activity can help separate your feelings; while you are angry at a particular thing, you love the person.

If this activity feels impossible, it may be a signal to take action. Consider what needs to be different, what needs to happen, and who or what can help make the changes happen.

2. Communicate: During the day, be creative with ways to tell your spouse of your love and appreciation. It does not need to be elaborate. A touch, a look, a smile, a word can change a day that is being lived on automatic pilot to a day that is an adventure in love.

3. Enjoy: At the end of the day, as you fall into bed, give a thought to waking with the intention of being open to the enjoyment of what the day will offer. Do this even if the day promises to hold things that you fear or dread. Often we see what we expect to see, not what is actually there.

NOTES

Patient notes: What are five things I am grateful for today?

Spouse notes: What are five things I am grateful for today?

CHAPTER 7

DESTINATION: DEATH

When treatment options have been exhausted and the cancer continues to grow, or when treatment itself becomes life-threatening and must be discontinued, the couple moves into the final stage of life for the patient, DESTINATION: DEATH. The reality is that everyone reaches this place at some point, but the luxury of cancer taking us there is that we generally know ahead of time that death is imminent. This awareness signals another shift in the couple's journey.

This is a time when the couple confronts the harshest realities of the entire journey, as they decide how they want to live out their remaining time together. When a couple lets go of searching and hoping for a cure, there is a shift into acceptance of the reality of death.

Paul and Geri were sitting in our office shortly after they began to shift into the phase regarding Paul's imminent death from cancer. Multiple surgeries and treatments over the past twelve months had been to no avail. Geri turned to Paul and lovingly said, "I am ready for you to die," and he replied, "I am ready, too." This couple had courageously stepped into perhaps the most honest and intimate place that two *people can experience together.*

RELATIONSHIP INTIMACY

During this stage of the journey, relationship intimacy becomes an absolute priority. It likely has been of great importance throughout the couple's journey with cancer; but at this point couples are willing to shove other things out of their way, if necessary, to ensure they have the kind and amount of time together that they desire. Social politeness and courtesies are dropped, if needed, in order to protect the sacred space that the couple has created.

Jim and Doris freely accepted visitors to their home during the earlier phases of Doris's cancer development, but in the DESTINATION: DEATH stage, they declined some visiting offers and made sure that most visits were kept to a brief amount of time. They wanted to use whatever energy Doris had for themselves, rather than spending this limited resource on others. Having always been very gracious and hospitable hosts before Doris's cancer, they at first felt guilty and rude for protecting her precious energy and moments of feeling physically better. Yet once they committed to this practice, it became easy because of the rewards they found within this new level of relationship intimacy.

In recalling how she and Paul had lived their final months before Paul died of cancer, Geri said there were some particular things they did as a couple and as a family with their three teenagers that helped each of them make it through this very challenging time.

Geri made Paul and their family her main focus during what turned out to be his last two months. She told him even on the day before he died that she would never, ever give up on him. All family members told Paul of their love for him, and he in turn shared his love for them. They made sure nothing was left unsaid. Geri and Paul always touched and made sure they told each other that they loved each other. Thanks to their talking and deliberate, shared intentions, Geri and Paul made the last two months of their life as a couple just as rich and full as possible. When Paul died, Geri had no regrets about how they had completed their journey together.

PATIENT AND CAREGIVER ROLES

Another issue facing couples during this final part of their journey together is that of protecting their relationship as husband and wife. It is difficult for the spouse to move out of, or stay out of, the role of being primarily a caregiver at the expense of being a spouse.

During Paul's last few months alive, a hospital bed was moved into their home. He required more and more physical assistance for bathing, body waste elimination, bedding changing, and so on. Geri and Paul decided that if Geri took on these increasing caregiver tasks, she would begin to feel more like a nurse than a wife, and that this would jeopardize their relationship intimacy. As a result of this realization, they jointly decided to seek outside help so that Paul could get the care he needed and the two of them could use the time they had together as husband and wife.

It is difficult for most of us to consider having strangers come into our home to help with the very personal care that is usually a part of this stage. The benefits of doing so are priceless, though, when the couple discovers the level of relationship intimacy that is possible when not distracted by caretaking tasks.

PREPARING FOR THE SPOUSE'S FUTURE

During this part of the couple's journey, discussion about the spouse's life after the patient dies is very important. If the couple is able to talk openly about this issue, there are decisions and plans that can be made that will help the spouse immediately following the patient's death and in the longer-term future.

One couple approached this issue by making a list of all the significant household repairs and remodeling projects needed; they then proceeded to complete the tasks prior to the husband's death. This tactic provided peace of mind to both partners by reassuring them that the surviving spouse would not have to deal with any of these tasks.

The wife of another couple taught her husband

how to use a sewing machine just prior to her own death; she wanted to be sure he would be prepared to meet the demands of living when she was no longer there to help him.

Another couple decided that prior to the husband's death, the wife needed to know how to manage her husband's private business and the investments he had always taken care of himself. They started setting aside times for the spouse to become informed and comfortable with these business issues so they could both feel a greater sense of peace about her financial security after his death. Other couples either write wills or update existing wills to ensure that estate issues do not add to the stress experienced by the surviving spouse.

Each couple will have their own unique matters to settle, and the more willing the patient and spouse are to talk openly, the greater the sense of peace and comfort that will be available to them.

SUPPORT

This is a particularly important time in the journey for the couple to have support for the kind of talking needed. Unfortunately, the people around us are quite often uncomfortable about hearing such open talking. Others may try to discourage such talking or thinking because they consider it fatalistic, morbid, or disrespectful. For this reason, the couple may find themselves without an arena to express these extremely important ideas, feelings, and plans. Within the Couples Facing Cancer support groups that we conduct, many couples say that no one else will talk with them about this stage of life and that they are grateful for the honest talking, support, and encouragement that occurs in these support groups. It is valuable for couples to find some accepting, encouraging place to hold these discussions, in addition to their own private conversations. If no couples groups exist in your community, perhaps one could be started just by contacting two or three other couples who are in a similar situation and asking if they would like to get together to talk and share.

Activities: Chapter 7

1. Prioritize: Commit to talking with your partner about the most important things for each and for both of you to focus on for the remainder of time you have together. Write the ideas down so you can both reference them to help stay on track. Decide that nothing else matters as much as what the two of you want, and begin to gently, but firmly, interact with others to create the space that you need as a couple and as a family.

NOTES

Patient notes:

Spouse notes:

2. Take Care of Unfinished Business: Together as a couple, decide what you want to have completed prior to the patient's death. Make a list if you have not already included these things in the above list, then decide how to accomplish them. This list may include things such as having special conversations with particular people. The patient may also want to communicate things from the heart that he or she wants others to know. The list could contain specific tasks to be completed that will help the surviving spouse live more comfortably or securely; it could include funeral plans; it could include writing or updating wills or any other postmortem wishes.

NOTES

Patient notes:

Spouse notes:

3. Nourish Spirituality: Together as a couple, continue talking and sharing about spiritual beliefs, even if you don't hold the same beliefs. It is important that you both feel understood and supported in your spiritual practice. If you so desire, meet with someone as a couple to talk more about your spirituality so that this area of your lives is fully explored and experienced.

4. Leave Nothing Unsaid

CHAPTER 8

DESTINATION: LIFE, CURE, REMISSION

DESTINATION: LIFE, CURE, REMISSION is the outcome that everyone hopes for, prays for, bargains for, strives for. It is the goal of weeks, months, and maybe years of effort, sacrifice, and intention. For couples, it is the ultimate victory of their team effort. Couples who have worked together will celebrate how they worked together as a team and needed each other in order to win. They will congratulate each other on taking charge, doing what needed to be done, and triumphing over the defeated foe called cancer. And then what often happens, even within minutes of receiving the diagnosis that the patient is cured, is a plummeting of the euphoric feelings. Questions emerge: Is it really over? Is it really gone? What now? How do we live now?

IS IT REALLY OVER? IS IT REALLY GONE?

Joan completed her last round of chemotherapy for breast cancer. She and Richard dressed up for their dinner out to celebrate. Joan fairly waltzed out to the car, singing, "It's over; it's over." When she sat in the car she dissolved in tears, saying, "It's never over. I'll always be someone with cancer. I'll never feel safe again."

Judy received the information that her colorectal cancer had disappeared; there were no signs of any malignant cells. She had undergone several courses of chemotherapy, had considered surgery, was told her tumor was "larger than we like to see" and " resistant." But now she was hearing that the chemo had worked, much to the professionals' surprise. She and Tom felt much relief and joy, followed immediately by fear and suspicion. They wondered if the cancer was really gone, or if the doctors had missed something; after all, she had felt fine before the diagnosis.

Carol received an e-mail from her friend at the conclusion of Bruce's treatment. Her friend shared her joy at Bruce's news and wondered how life was now that Bruce was well. Carol studied the e-mail. While she appreciated her friend's good intentions, she was aware that Bruce had been pronounced "cured" five years ago, following his first diagnosis, and the cancer had returned. She and Bruce would always live with the knowledge that cancer is a possibility.

These couples are not pessimistic. They are experiencing the reality that others who have not lived with cancer can more easily deny. The reality is that there are no guarantees and that we are all indeed vulnerable to disease and death. This is not a prescription to live in fear and pessimism. It can be the opportunity, the wake-up call, to live life in the fullest quality and with the greatest of joy. It can mean living with a conscious awareness of the delicate miracle that life truly is, whether or not a cancer diagnosis has been received. How sad it is that many forget that life itself is a terminal condition and live it thoughtlessly.

WHAT NOW? HOW DO WE LIVE NOW?

Many couples experience that, during the treatment phase of living with cancer, they were focused on survival. There were many things that needed to be done in order to complete the treatment. The patient likely was focused on the impact of the treatment, how he or she felt, and how to be as physically healthy as possible in order to survive the treatment and overcome the cancer. The spouse was likely frantically busy with keeping the household running and picking up the slack for all the activities the patient was unable to do. When the patient is then pronounced "cured," the couple may experience a flood of overwhelming responsibility and choices as they think through what happens next. Each spouse is acutely aware of the fragility of life. Each may have his or her own ideas about how to best live.

The patient may now have a changed body. Many times the aggressive treatment needed to fight cancer causes irrevocable changes. Surgeries may leave a person permanently disfigured or disabled. Chemotherapy may cause permanent body or energy changes. The treatment may have caused damage to the extent that further treatment is necessary for correcting or counteracting. Once survival has been assured, the task is now to adapt and accommodate to the changes.

Finally, the two individuals likely have changed emotionally and psychologically. The spouse may have learned that after needing to be strong and independent to keep the household running, he or she may not want to return to the prior role. The patient may have new desires regarding work time versus play time. Either may have a different level or type of spirituality than before. There are a myriad of adjustments to be made, just when the couple may be physically and emotionally exhausted from the experience of treatment and the focus on survival.

Carol and Bruce had a business together. They worked long hours together and had a joint ethic of work first, play later. During the marathon treatment phase, Carol necessarily picked up much of the work that Bruce had previously done. She worked even longer hours to keep the business going, upholding their dream so that when Bruce was well it would be there for him and for them. When Bruce was pronounced cured, he resented Carol's constant focus on work. His life view had become "life is now." He was well aware that he could no longer confidently work toward good times during retirement. He wanted Carol to join him in having fun together today. They began to discuss selling their business and building a different kind of life to reflect who they were now.

When a couple is faced with cancer, each stage of the journey is a journey in and of itself. DESTINATION: LIFE, CURE, REMISSION is a stage that encompasses being on the very top of a mountain of joy and plummeting to the depths of discouragement. Together, after the extremes have been experienced, the couple can hike slowly, thoughtfully, and deliberately to a consciously decided way of living that reflects quality of life and expressions of love.

Couples that have been cured for many, many years tell of how cancer continues to influence how they live. Chuck tells of his spouse continuing to live, strong and healthy, twenty-two years after treatment, and how they are still grateful for each and every day. Eighteen years later, Robert tells of the angel he still experiences in his heart, protecting him and Dot and guiding them to live in joy and love.

DIFFERENT PATHS

For couples who have struggled in their relationships, this may be the time to make the difficult decision that it is not in their individual best interests to be together. The impact of being confronted with the fragility of life may propel them to decide that being a couple does not add to the quality of life. It may be that both would have a better chance of living fully and happily if they were not married to each other.

As couples review who they are and how they want to live, the conclusion may be reached that the changes needed to make this a quality relationship are not possible. Perhaps, for whatever reason, the couple has been unhappy for a long time and did not take the action to change or leave the situation. After a bout with cancer, an individual is often no longer willing to put up with anything unhealthy in life, whether it be a style of living, a job, or a relationship.

If you find yourself considering that ending the marriage is the answer, contact and work with a marriage counselor. Entering marriage counseling may or may not have the goal of saving the marriage. It is very legitimate to use counseling to make sure that you have really looked at the situation from all angles, considered every option, and given the relationship a fair chance to change. If the decision is to end the marriage, that does not reflect failure of the counseling or the individuals. Committing to working with a counselor for a period of time can provide the important ingredient of ensuring that the decision to end a relationship is not impulsive or an emotional reaction.

Even though the activities at the end of this chapter are intended to build and enhance a couple's relationship, some of them may be of assistance if you find yourselves considering taking different life paths at this point. Activities Two and Three provide a structure to review carefully and thoughtfully the journey you have just completed and to consider what lies ahead.

Activities: Chapter 8

1. Celebrate: Choose a form of celebration that is meaningful to you as a couple. Enter into it celebrating what has been accomplished, with no strings attached concerning the future. Many couples find they want to celebrate in one way privately, with just the two of them, in addition to celebrating with those professional helpers, friends, and family who have been there with love and support.

2. Review: As a couple, sit down or take a walk and review the journey from start to finish. Talk about it, discuss it, consider the events along with the feelings and the learnings.

NOTES

Patient notes:

Spouse notes:

3. Compare and Discuss: Talk about: Where were we? Where are we now?

a. as individuals

b. as a couple

Take some time to journal and write about your observations before you talk together. Remember the listening techniques you learned in Chapter Five. Focus on really understanding and listening to what your spouse is telling you. Remember: that person may be changed from the one you thought you knew so well.

4. Act on Your Intentions: When the two of you feel you know what is most important in how you live out your lives and your relationship, write down what someone outside your relationship would be able to see as evidence that you are living out these intentions. This is very important. If you don't actually act in a way that is visible to live out your desires, all the intentions in your heart are just so much dust in the wind. For the behaviors that are intimate and private, consider what an angel or spirit would see! Then make an appointment with yourselves — write it on your calendars — to meet every three months to check on whether you are acting on your intentions and if you want to change them in any way. By doing this, you will guarantee that you will not slip into living carelessly, wasting the precious days you have together.

NOTES

Patient notes: I commit to ...

Spouse notes: I commit to ...

5. Use the Tools: Go back to the "Tools for the Journey" chapter. The tools that were so important to maintaining a strong relationship during this journey are equally important in maintaining your relationship during normal life. Make sure you have a copy of ONE DAY AT A TIME in many places where you will notice it. When you come across this list, use it as a reminder to activate any of the tools that have grown stale or have been forgotten.

Epilogue

Your journey with cancer has begun, whether as patient, spouse, friend, relative, or helper. For those of you who are friends, relatives, or helpers, we hope this book helps you to understand and support the work that a couple facing cancer has to do. For those of you who are cancer patients or spouses of cancer patients, we wish you well on your journey. No matter how much time has elapsed since you started the journey, you can look back with awe at the many miles you have traveled. If you have been recently diagnosed, you may feel as if you are traveling at the speed of light while trying to comprehend the impact of the diagnosis. If you were diagnosed months or years ago, the journey may feel like a long, slow hike.

Many who travel with cancer attest to the fact that bitterness and despair have visited them. With love and hard work, you may be able to say that you did experience them but were able to leave them along the side of the road and travel on.

For couples facing cancer, the journey offers more than grief and loss; it can also bring abundance. Holding hands, literally and figuratively, with your life partner throughout the cancer experience is a blessing that will add quality and meaning to the whole of your life.

Our wish is that, together, you will find the joy of intimacy at its deepest level as you travel this journey with cancer and its treatment. The fear and the sadness will find you easily enough. Put your energy and determination toward living in your hearts each day rather than saving these times of closeness for later.

We also wish that, together, you will find strength and courage in the face of such a formidable foe as cancer. As quoted in the epigraph of this book, Pete challenged himself to refuse to let cancer ruin his life — even though it would likely kill him. His stated intention has been a wonderful source of courage for us. If Pete's challenge speaks to you, please take it with you.

Do not let cancer ruin your lives. Reach for the gifts this journey will certainly reveal.

Resources

American Cancer Society

Information and referrals to numerous support services.

1599 Clifton Road, NE
Atlanta, GA 30329
(800) ACS-2345
www.cancer.org

American Association for Marriage and Family Therapy

Information on qualified marital counseling support in your area.

1133 15th Street, NW Suite 300
Washington, DC 20005-2710
(202) 452-0109
http://www.aamft.org

American Association of Sex Educators, Counselors, and Therapists

Names of therapists in your area who might assist with problems in sexual relationships that develop from cancer and its treatment.

435 North Michigan Avenue
Chicago, IL 60611
(312) 644-0828

Cancer Care

A national, nonprofit organization that helps people with cancer, their families and professional caregivers. Direct services nationally through its Counseling Line (1-800-813-HOPE).

1180 Avenue of the Americas
New York, NY 10036
(212) 302-2400
http://www.cancercare.org

Cancer Conquerors Foundation

Programs emphasizing mind/body/spirit integration.

P.O. Box 3444
Fullerton, CA 92634
(800) 238-6479

Cancer Guidance Hotline

A networking service to connect you with trained volunteers who have experienced cancer themselves or in their families.

1323 Forbes Avenue
Pittsburgh, PA 15219
(412) 261-2211

Couples Facing Cancer™

A network of couples providing support to surmount the relationship challenges of cancer and its treatment. This new group is still forming local chapters. Call for information or consultation on starting a group in your area.

P.O. Box 272964
Fort Collins, CO 80527-2964
(888) 256-6117
E-mail: CouFacCan@aol.com
http://www.couplesfacingcancer.com

Make Today Count

An organization that provides emotional support.

c/o Connie Zimmerman
Mid America Cancer Center
1235 East Cherokee
Springfield, MO 65804-2263
(800) 432-2273

National Coalition for Cancer Survivorship

Support for cancer survivors and their families.

5th Floor
1010 Wayne Avenue
Silver Springs, MD 20910
(301) 650-8868

The Wellness Community (National Office)

National network of cancer support centers. The centers offer sharing groups, support groups, family groups, and educational groups.

2716 Ocean Park Boulevard, Suite 1040
Santa Monica, CA 90405
(310) 314-2555

Recommended Reading

Books

1. Albom, Mitch. *Tuesdays with Morrie.* New York: Doubleday, 1997.

2. Beck, Aaron T. *Love Is Never Enough.* New York: Harper & Row Publishers, 1988.

3. Benson, Herbert. *Timeless Healing.* New York: Fireside, 1996.

4. Borysenko, Joan. *Minding the Body, Mending the Mind.* New York: Bantam, 1987.

5. Borysenko, John and Borysenko, Joan. *The Power of the Mind to Heal.* Carson: Hay House, 1994.

6. Brigham, Deirdre Davis. *Imagery for Getting Well.* New York: Norton, 1994.

7. Chodron, Pema. *When Things Fall Apart.* Boston: Shambala, 1997.

8. Chopra, Deepak. *Quantum Healing.* New York: Bantam, 1989.

9. Dossey, Larry. *Healing Words.* New York: HarperCollins Publishers, 1993.

10. Groopman, Jerome. *The Measure of Our Days.* New York: Viking, 1997.

11. Hilts, Elizabeth. *Getting In Touch With Your Inner Bitch.* Bridgeport: Hysteria Publications, 1994.

12. Kabat-Zinn, Jon. *Full Catastrophe Living.* New York: Delta, 1991.

13. Lerner, Harriet. *The Dance of Intimacy.* New York: Harper & Row Publishers, 1989.

14. Lerner, Michael. *Choices in Healing.* Cambridge: MIT Press, 1994.

15. Levine, Stephen. *Healing into Life and Death.* New York: Doubleday, 1987.

16. Remen, Rachel Naomi. *Kitchen Table Wisdom.* New York: Riverhead Books, 1996.

17. Remen, Rachel Naomi. *Wounded Healers.* Bolinas: Wounded Healer Press, 1994.

18. Sark. *Succulent Wild Woman.* New York: Fireside, 1997.

19. Schwartz, Morrie. *Letting Go.* New York: Delta, 1996.

20. Siegel, Bernie S. *Love, Medicine and Miracles.* New York: Harper & Row Publishers, 1986.

21. Siegel, Bernie S. *Peace, Love and Healing.* New York: Harper & Row Publishers, 1989.

22. Watts, Alan. *The Wisdom of Insecurity.* New York: Vintage, 1951.

Articles

23. Fields, Rick. "Slow Dancing with the Rhino." *Utne Reader* (March/April 1998): 73-75.

24. Harvard Mental Health Letter."Cancer and the Mind." *Harvard Mental Health Letter* (March 1998): 14-19.

25. Rolland, John S. "In Sickness and In Health: The Impact of Illness on Couples' Relationships." *Journal of Marriage and Family Therapy* (October 1994): 20-24; 327-347.

26. Simmons, Philip. "On Getting Up in the Morning." *World* (November/December 1997): xi-9; 40-45.

27. Skubik, Suzanne. "Body, Mind and Soul." *World* (September/October 1997):15-19.

28. "Life with Cancer: How to Provide Support." *Women's Health Advocate.* (September 1996): 4-6.

About the Authors

Jan Latona, Ph.D., received her doctorate in counseling psychology in 1987 from the University of Illinois. She has provided counseling for individuals, couples, families, and groups through private practice and in agency and university settings. Jan is currently vice president for clinical services for Employee Assistance Programs International.

Gary J. Stricklin, Ph.D., holds a doctorate in marriage and family therapy from Kansas State University. In his 24 years in the mental health profession, he has worked in a variety of settings including private practice, mental health centers, and school systems. He was one of the founders and also the director of Hospice of Decatur County in Oberlin, Kansas. Currently, he provides consultation to national corporate clients concerning mental health and workplace issues.

Jan and Gary, who live in Fort Collins, Colorado, are married to each other and between them have four adult sons. Their own journeys with cancer began in 1993. Jan's first husband died shortly after being diagnosed with cancer. Gary was diagnosed with cancer in 1993 and again in 1997 after he and

Jan were married. Along with their professional training and experience, the roles they have played as cancer patient and spouse have added depth and understanding to their counseling of other couples dealing with cancer.

Couples Facing Cancer: Support Groups and Seminars

Jan Latona and Gary Stricklin are co-founders of a program called Couples Facing Cancer™ (CFC). The program offers consulting and training services, as well as support groups, for couples who are dealing with cancer. The primary focus of these services is understanding the impact of this life-threatening disease and its treatment on the couple's relationship.

Support Groups

Cancer patients and their spouses attend the support group sessions together. These groups provide a forum for discussing, problem solving, and receiving support to meet the challenges posed by cancer. Each couple experiences identified, predictable stages from the time of diagnosis to the patient's recovery or death. Each of the stages impacts the couple's relationship in a particular way and, in turn, raises specific relationship challenges.

Drs. Latona and Stricklin have seen that, when successfully addressed, these challenges can yield greater levels of relationship intimacy than ever before experienced; when avoided, these challenges can threaten the stability and intimacy of even strong relationships.

Members of Couples Facing Cancer™ support groups have been enthusiastic about benefits received from these groups. The following are a few of their comments:

"Even though I lost my husband to cancer, the friendship and encouragement he got from the support group always gave him hope. The support group members were blessings in our lives."

"Before the group I was on auto-pilot, trying to take care of everything and everyone — but me. The group showed me that taking care of me was in everyone's best interest."

"You are not really out there alone — unless you choose to be. It's okay to admit you need help and to ask for it."

"Sometimes it surprises me what my spouse holds in and doesn't share with me one-on-one. The group allows the feelings and thoughts to come out."

"Hearing someone else's story helped me to realize we're not alone. I learned a lot from others about how they made it through difficult times."

"Our conversations in the group were not superficial. The group is about life — learning how to face death so that we can live."

"If I can be with my spouse through this, what greater gift can I give him?"

Seminars and Consultation

Dr. Latona and Dr. Stricklin, both experienced trainers, provide seminars and programs, regionally and nationally for the general public and helping professionals, regarding cancer and its impact on the relationship between patient and spouse. Both brief and extensive programs are offered.

Seminars, workshops and consultation are available for the following audiences:

- *Couples who are facing cancer*
  Brief seminars and extended workshop retreats

- *Facilitators of Couples Facing Cancer™ support groups*
  Facilitator training at no cost other than travel and lodging expenses to assist in forming community-based CFC groups

- *Mental health professionals and medical professionals*
  Guidelines and strategies for professional helpers working with patients facing cancer

For information:
Call Couples Facing Cancer™ at 1-888-256-6117 or visit its web site http://www.couplesfacingcancer.com

NOTES

NOTES

NOTES

Quick Order Form

Fax orders: 1-888-256-6117   **Telephone orders:** 1-888-256-6117
Postal orders: Greyrock Publishing
                   PO Box 272964, Fort Collins, CO 80527-2964
E-mail orders: GreyrockP@aol.com

Please send me:

_____ copies of *Love is a Journey: Couples Facing Cancer™* @ $14.95
per copy.

                                              Subtotal _____

_____ laminated "One Day at a Time" postcard size cards @ $.50 each

                                              Subtotal _____

Sales tax:
Please add 6.75 % for products shipped to Colorado addresses _____

Shipping:
   US: $3 for the first book and $1.50 for each additional book _____
                          International: Call for prices _____

                                        TOTAL _____

Payment: __ Check

                    __ Credit Card: __ Visa   __ MasterCard

Card number: _____

Name on card: _____ Exp. date: _____ / _____

Signature: _____

Please send free information on:

_____ Consulting   _____ Speaking / Seminars

_____ How to start a Couples Facing Cancer™ support group.

Name: _____

Address: _____

City: _____ State: _____ Zip: _____

Telephone: _____

E-mail address: _____

Quick Order Form

Fax orders: 1-888-286-8117. Telephone orders: 1-888-286-8117.
Postal orders: Greycloak Publishing
PO Box 270984, Fort Collins, CO 80527-0984
E-mail orders: Graycloak@aol.com

___ Please send me:

_____ copies of Love is a Journey, Couples Facing Cancer™ @ $14.95
per copy

_____ Subtotal

_____ laminated "One Day at a Time" postcard/mug cards @ $3.50 each

_____ Subtotal

_____ Sales tax:
Please add 8.3% for products shipped to Colorado addresses

_____ Shipping:
US $5 for the first book and $1.50 for each additional book.
International/Call for prices

_____ TOTAL

Payment: _____ Check
Credit Card: _____ Visa _____ MasterCard

Card number:

Name on card: _____ Exp. date: _____

Signature:

Please send free information on:

_____ Consulting _____ Speaking/Seminars
_____ How to start a Couples Facing Cancer™ support group

Name:
Address:
City: _____ State: _____ Zip:
Telephone:
E-mail address:

Quick Order Form

Fax orders: 1-888-256-6117   **Telephone orders:** 1-888-256-6117
Postal orders: Greyrock Publishing
                  PO Box 272964, Fort Collins, CO 80527-2964
E-mail orders: GreyrockP@aol.com

Please send me:

_____ copies of *Love is a Journey: Couples Facing Cancer*™ @ $14.95
per copy.

                                                       Subtotal _____

_____ laminated "One Day at a Time" postcard size cards @ $.50 each

                                                       Subtotal _____

Sales tax:
Please add 6.75 % for products shipped to Colorado addresses _____

Shipping:
      US: $3 for the first book and $1.50 for each additional book _____
                               International: Call for prices _____

                                                TOTAL _____

Payment: __ Check

                  __ Credit Card: __ Visa   __ MasterCard

Card number: _____

Name on card: _____ Exp. date: _____ / _____

Signature: _____

Please send free information on:

_____ Consulting   _____ Speaking / Seminars

_____ How to start a Couples Facing Cancer™ support group.

Name: _____

Address: _____

City: _____ State: _____ Zip: _____

Telephone: _____

E-mail address: _____

Quick Order Form

Fax orders: 1-888-256-6117 **Telephone orders:** 1-888-256-6117
Postal orders: Greyrock Publishing
PO Box 272964, Fort Collins, CO 80527-2964
E-mail orders: GreyrockP@aol.com

Please send me:

_____ copies of *Love is a Journey: Couples Facing Cancer™* @ $14.95
per copy.

Subtotal _____

_____ laminated "One Day at a Time" postcard size cards @ $.50 each

Subtotal _____

Sales tax:
Please add 6.75 % for products shipped to Colorado addresses _____

Shipping:
US: $3 for the first book and $1.50 for each additional book _____
International: Call for prices _____

TOTAL _____

Payment: __ Check

__ Credit Card: __ Visa __ MasterCard

Card number: _____

Name on card: _____ Exp. date: _____ / _____

Signature: _____

Please send free information on:

_____ Consulting _____ Speaking / Seminars

_____ How to start a Couples Facing Cancer™ support group.

Name: _____

Address: _____

City: _____ State: _____ Zip: _____

Telephone: _____

E-mail address: _____